WASTE MINIMIZAT

A Practical Guide

C000089544

Barry Crittenden and Stan Kolaczkowski

INSTITUTION OF CHEMICAL ENGINEERS

The information in this book is given in good
faith and belief in its accuracy, but does not
imply the acceptance of any legal liability or
responsibility whatsoever, by the Institution, or
by the authors, for the consequences of its use
or misuse in any particular circumstances.

Published by
Institution of Chemical Engineers,
Davis Building,
165–189 Railway Terrace,
Rugby, Warwickshire CV21 3HQ, UK.

Copyright © 1995 Institution of Chemical Engineers
A Registered Charity

Reprinted 1995

ISBN 0 85295 342 9

Printed in the United Kingdom by Galliard (Printers) Ltd, Great Yarmouth.

PREFACE

Preparation of the first edition of this guide was commissioned by the Institution of Chemical Engineers with the support of the Department of the Environment and under the guidance of a steering committee formed from people experienced in waste minimization projects. 1000 draft copies of the guide were produced and freely circulated to obtain feedback on its usefulness to UK process engineering and related industries. The result is this practical guide on waste minimization for engineers and their managers, focusing largely on the process and related industries. However, the potential clearly exists to extend and adapt the methodology to a much broader range of industries. Case studies and examples are included to demonstrate the gains which can be made from implementing waste minimization projects. The guide has been edited so as to be complementary to the IChemE's Waste Minimization Training Package[1].

Since relatively little information on the subject has been published in the UK, the contents of the guide are based largely, but not exclusively, on the *Waste Minimization Opportunity Assessment Manual*[2] and the *Draft Guide for an Effective Pollution Prevention Program*[3], published by the US Environmental Protection Agency, and the booklets entitled *Cutting Your Losses*[4,5] published by the UK Department of Trade and Industry. The Institution of Chemical Engineers gratefully acknowledges the Hazardous Waste Engineering Research Laboratory, Office of Research and Development, US Environmental Protection Agency, Cincinnati, Ohio, and the UK Department of Trade and Industry for the use made by the authors of these documents.

Whilst this book is written primarily for readers in the UK, the techniques, methodology and examples provided are nonetheless universally applicable; clearly readers outside the UK need to take due account of their own national legislation.

SUMMARY

Waste minimization is an important element of sustainable development. It is concerned with environmental protection and with the reduction of production costs by the reduction of waste at source and by recycling. This guide has been written to provide introductions to the many practical techniques which can be implemented to minimize waste, ranging from simple good housekeeping practice to sophisticated computational and life cycle methods. The book also provides a widely accepted methodology which can be followed to ensure that waste minimization programmes and projects are successfully implemented.

Accepting that the complete elimination of waste is unlikely to be a realistic goal, the preferred approach to waste minimization is reduction of waste at source, including good housekeeping and changes to technology, raw materials and products, and recycling, both on-site and off-site. The guide has been written to cover both existing production facilities and the design of new and hence 'cleaner' processes.

Many successful projects involve combinations of waste minimization approaches and it should not be assumed, for example, that recycling is a less preferable way of dealing with waste. The reader is also encouraged to explore whether what is currently described as a waste on an existing production site may in fact be a resource or product in its own right.

It has been assumed that a company has established an environmental policy, and perhaps an environmental management system, which includes minimization of all wastes, including those to landfill, incineration, liquid effluent and to gaseous discharge. Whilst this guide has been written primarily for process engineers working in production and design environments, those managerial aspects which directly impact on waste minimization programmes have been included for the sake of completeness.

HOW TO USE THIS GUIDE

Chapter 1 provides a background to the environmental and regulatory pressures which are the drivers to environmental improvement programmes, and Chapter 2 provides a summary of all the benefits, whether financial, environmental, health or safety, which can be accrued following the implementation of waste minimization programmes and projects. Chapter 3 summarizes some of the hurdles to waste minimization and the need for company and senior management commitment.

Substantial chapters deal with waste minimization methodology (Chapter 4) and practical techniques, with example case studies (Chapter 5). The engineer engaged in the design of new and 'cleaner' processes is referred particularly to the design methodologies and toolkits described in Chapter 5. The sections in Chapter 5 on changes to technology, raw materials and products, and on recycling are also relevant. The engineer engaged in work on existing production facilities needs to start by considering whether any further progress can be made in the area described as 'good practice' in Chapter 5. Substantial progress can often be made with short pay-backs in this area of waste minimization and the project methodology described in Chapter 4 should be followed. Changes to technology, to raw materials and to products on existing production facilities, as described in Chapter 5, normally require that formal technical and economic evaluations are made before capital expenditure can be authorized. For this purpose the methodology described in Chapter 4 should be adapted to suit a company's preferred procedures. As many of the benefits described in Chapter 2 as possible should be included in the economic evaluation.

The US Environmental Protection Agency makes extensive use of worksheets for the assessment and evaluation phases of its waste minimization methodology. Chapter 6 gives listings and some examples of these worksheets. Chapter 7 provides information on typical wastes, causes and controlling factors in plant operations; Chapter 8 provides sources of practical waste minimization techniques.

The subject of waste minimization is developing rapidly and in many instances only overviews of techniques have been provided in this guide. The References (Chapter 9) and Further Reading (Chapter 10) should be used to fill any gaps and IChemE publications such as the *Environmental Protection Bulletin* and *Process Safety and Environmental Protection* (Part B of IChemE's *Transactions*) should be followed regularly. In addition it is recommended that the IChemE's Environmental Training Packages, including that on Waste Minimization, be used for interactive training.

CONTENTS

1. INTRODUCTION AND BACKGROUND TO WASTE MINIMIZATION

Liquid, solid and gaseous waste materials can be generated during the manufacture of any product. Apart from creating potential environmental problems, wastes not only represent losses from the production process of valuable raw materials and energy, but also require significant investment in pollution control practices. Industrial waste treatment has often been viewed as an addition to the end of a process, offering little scope to recover value from the waste material. Worse still, many 'end-of-pipe' waste treatment techniques do not actually eliminate the waste but simply transfer it from one environmental medium to another (air, water, land), often in a highly diluted form.

The UK Environmental Protection Act 1990 (EPA 1990) requires a continuing reappraisal by the process industries of waste management practices, as improved techniques including technology become available and regulatory requirements are progressively introduced. It is likely that, as further restrictions are placed on the disposal of substances to environmental media, the costs of waste treatment and disposal will continue to rise. Against this background, there will be increasing incentives to minimize the generation of waste. Thus waste minimization should be viewed as a concept which will assist company efforts to meet environmental requirements and reduce operating costs.

A waste minimization strategy is therefore a most important component of a company's environmental management system.

1.1   DEFINITIONS AND SYNONYMS

Process industry waste represents a loss of raw materials, intermediates, by-products or main products which require time, manpower and money to manage. More formally, Section 75 of EPA 1990 defines waste as:

(a) any substance which constitutes a scrap material or an effluent, or other unwanted surplus substance arising from the application of a process; and

(b) any substance or article which requires to be disposed of as being broken, worn out, contaminated or otherwise spoiled.

The definition covers anything which is discarded or otherwise dealt with as if it were waste, unless the contrary is proved, and includes:

• liquids or solid residues from a process;
• contaminated materials;

1

- off-specification products;
- accidental spillages and associated cleaning materials;
- machine/finishing residues;
- fugitive emissions;
- gaseous discharges.

Examples of typical wastes from plant operations, together with the causes and controlling factors in waste generation, are provided in Chapter 7.

Further UK and European Commission (EC) definitions of controlled waste, special waste, hazardous waste, toxic waste, dangerous waste, waste oil, inert waste, non-hazardous waste, difficult waste and clinical waste are provided by *Croner's Waste Management*[6]. Reference should also be made to the IChemE guide on *Management of Waste in the Process Industries*[7], due for publication in mid-1995.

Waste minimization involves any technique, process or activity which either avoids, eliminates or reduces a waste at its source, usually within the confines of the production unit, or allows reuse or recycling of the waste for benign purposes. Synonymous terms include:
- waste minimization;
- waste reduction;
- clean or cleaner technologies, engineering, processing;
- pollution prevention/reduction;
- environmental technologies;
- low and non-waste technologies.

For new and hence 'cleaner' processes it is, in general, better to use the design, research and development stages to avoid the generation of waste than to modify a process once it has been installed.

For most new projects which require planning permission, an environmental assessment needs to be made, and an environmental statement prepared for consultation with the public and interested bodies. Even for new projects which do not fall under the Environmental Impact Assessment Regulations, it is desirable that environmental assessments are integrated into each stage of the planning and design processes. The generation, transportation and disposal of wastes, in all forms, would normally be key elements of the environmental assessments. The earlier the assessment is made in the planning and design processes, and hence the earlier an opportunity is taken to identify options available for process and technology alternatives to avoid potential environmental problems, the less likely it is that the project will require expensive changes in the future.

Whilst emphasis is placed in this guide on the word 'waste', all emissions of materials into air, water and land, as well as energy consumption, should be considered in waste minimization programmes.

1.2 LEGISLATION AND COMPLIANCE

It is inappropriate in this book to provide a detailed account of legislation pertaining to the generation, treatment and disposal of waste, particularly since this subject is thoroughly covered and regularly updated elsewhere — for example, in *Croner's Waste Management*[6]. However, EPA 1990 covers a wide range of environmental topics, many of which are relevant to waste management. Waste disposal, pollution control and nuisance limitation are covered by the provision of the Control of Pollution Act 1974 (COPA 1974) until the full legislative provisions of EPA 1990 are implemented.

1.2.1 INTEGRATED POLLUTION CONTROL

Part I of EPA 1990 implemented with effect from 1 April 1991 introduced the new concept of Integrated Pollution Control (IPC) which applies to the release of pollutants to air, water and land from certain processes and establishes the concept of Best Available Techniques Not Entailing Excessive Cost (BATNEEC) which must be used to prevent and, only where that is not practicable, to minimize pollution. 'Techniques' of BATNEEC are defined as including not only technical means and technology but also operating procedures and design, construction and layout.

Part I of EPA 1990 establishes two tiers of pollution control. Those industries which give rise to the most serious pollution problems or which have the greatest potential for multimedia pollution have been designated Part A processes and fall under the system of IPC, the aim of which is to achieve the Best Practicable Environmental Option (BPEO) through using BATNEEC. This is intended to help to ensure that the overall environmental impact (on air, water and land) of each process is minimized. Authorizations by Her Majesty's Inspectorate of Pollution (HMIP) are required for Part A processes, and applications must include, amongst many other things, information on the proposed releases to each environmental medium of polluting substances during both normal and foreseeably abnormal operating conditions. It is intended that the information should include the concentrations and quantities of wastes which go to an off-site landfill, as well as details of substances which could be released to the land in the vicinity of the plant. Clearly, it now becomes necessary to make detailed assessments which, as will be seen in Section 4.3 (page 17), are similar to those which are necessary for the implementation of waste minimization projects.

In granting an authorization, HMIP will make general conditions which, amongst others, include the condition that releases must not constitute a breach of any statutory limits, standards or objectives, including limits laid down in EU (formerly EC) directives. In addition, an authorization may include specific conditions which, for example, limit the amount or composition of any substance produced by, or utilized in, a process. Thus, irrespective of any commercial advantage or disadvantage arising from the implementation of a waste minimization programme, it will be necessary to achieve compliance with environmental regulations and standards.

Certain less seriously polluting industries are designated Part B processes and fall, in respect of emissions to air only, under the parallel system of Local Authority Pollution Control. The Water Resources Act 1991 regulates aqueous discharges from industrial (and other) processes which do not fall under IPC.

1.2.2   DEPOSIT OF CONTROLLED WASTE ON LAND

Part II of EPA 1990 replaces Part I of COPA 1974, and deals specifically with the deposit of Controlled Waste on land. Part II, amongst other things, places responsibility (the Duty of Care) for Controlled Waste on waste producers, and on all who handle waste. Regulations impose record-keeping obligations on those subject to the Duty of Care which, amongst other things, include an accurate description of the waste. Again, this information is of direct value in making assessments for a waste minimization programme (see Section 4.3 on page 17).

1.2.3   SPECIAL WASTES

Section 17 of COPA 1974 made provision for regulations to cover the movement of wastes which are particularly hazardous. The Control of Pollution (Special Waste) Regulations 1980 came into force in 1981. Their provision, amongst other things, includes a consignment note system with a register of consignment notes to be kept by producers, carriers and disposers. This information is also of direct value in making assessments for a waste minimization programme (see Section 4.3 on page 17).

It is important to note that whilst the Control of Pollution (Special Waste) Regulations 1980 fulfil the Government's obligations under the EC Directive on Toxic and Dangerous Wastes (78/319/EEC), there were a number of subsequent EC developments which caused the UK Government to publish a Consultation Paper on new Special Waste Regulations (February 1990). The consignment note system may be altered at some stage in the future.

1.3   HIERARCHY OF WASTE MANAGEMENT PRACTICES

The UK subscribes to the hierarchy of waste management options set down in the European Community Council Resolution on Waste Policy (90/C122/02) and in the revised Waste Framework Directive (91/156/EEC). This hierarchy, shown in Figure 1, indicates that prevention — that is, stopping waste being formed in the first place — is the preferred option. The goal of zero waste generation is probably unachievable in any activity and therefore the relative positions of various waste management options are shown in a rather more practical and generally accepted waste management hierarchy in Figure 2.

Waste minimization is concerned with the first, second and third levels in the hierarchy shown in Figure 2 — that is, with elimination, reduction at source and recycling — and companies should strive to elevate waste management practices to these highest options, since conceptually it makes more sense to avoid producing a waste rather than to develop extensive treatment schemes.

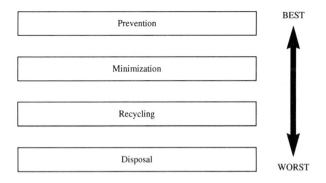

Prevention	BEST
Minimization	
Recycling	
Disposal	WORST

Figure 1   Hierarchy of waste management options in EC Council Resolution on Waste Policy (91/156/EEC).

Elimination	Complete elimination of waste	
Reduction at source	The avoidance, reduction or elimination of waste, generally within the confines of the production unit, through changes in industrial processes or procedures	Highest priority
Recycling	The use, reuse and recycling of wastes for the original or some other purpose such as input material, materials recovery or energy production	
Treatment	The destruction, detoxification, neutralization, etc, of wastes into less harmful substances	
Disposal	The release of wastes to air, water, or land in properly controlled or safe ways so as to render them harmless; secure land disposal may involve volume reduction, encapsulation, leachate containment and monitoring techniques	Lowest priority

Figure 2   Hierarchy of waste management practices.

Source reduction and recycling techniques are described in Sections 5.1 and 5.2 respectively (pages 41 and 48).

Waste minimization is, in most cases, not concerned with:

• actions taken after the waste has been generated — that is, incineration, detoxification, thermal, chemical or biological decomposition, stabilization through solidification, embedding or encapsulation are specifically excluded. (It should be noted that there are instances where destruction can be the only method — for example, for chemicals which are no longer produced, perhaps for environmental reasons. Examples include polychlorinated biphenyls and certain pesticides);

• actions that only dilute the waste constituents for hazard or toxicity reduction;

• actions that only transfer waste constituents from one environmental medium to another — for example, off-gas scrubbing to transfer a hazardous constituent from air to water.

It is clear therefore that all emissions to air, water and soil, as well as energy consumption of raw materials and utilities, should be considered as part of a waste minimization programme.

1.4   ENERGY CONSERVATION ASPECTS

Energy recovery is a well-established practice in the process industries. Heat exchange integration techniques such as 'pinch technology', which aim to reduce the net amount of energy put into a process at the hot end and taken out at the cold end, now normally form an integral part of process design.

Energy recovery activities themselves can often reduce pollution and waste generation. For example, a reduction in energy consumption decreases the quantity of fossil fuels burned, and thus decreases the amount of air pollutants generated. Reduced boiler operation also reduces the discharge of cooling water and boiler blowdowns. A reduction in the amount of boiler feed water requires less use of chemicals for treatment purposes. In addition, since waste minimization projects are concerned with minimizing the total use of resources, so their implementation should also result in more efficient use of energy, and hence financial savings.

Furthermore, since most treatment and destruction processes (such as incineration and biological oxidation) are net consumers of utilities, financial savings should be possible by reducing the amount of waste generated.

2.   BENEFITS OF WASTE MINIMIZATION

Waste minimization can provide long-term benefits in two ways. First, it can assist the attainment of, and improvement on, regulatory requirements. Second, it can provide a company with opportunities to improve profitability by:
- realizing specific economic benefits;
- reducing liabilities;
- promoting a positive public image;
- improving the health and safety of employees;
- increasing operating efficiency and hence reducing production costs.

Waste minimization projects must be evaluated in the same manner as a business opportunity. The implementation of a waste minimization project is likely to incur additional capital investment, which may be rewarded by benefits such as:
- reduced on-site waste monitoring, control and treatment costs;
- reduced handling, pretreatment, transport and off-site disposal costs;
- reduced waste storage space, thereby creating more space for productive operations;
- reduced administrative and paperwork costs associated with waste disposal;
- reduced analytical costs for the identification and characterization of specific waste streams;
- reduced production costs, including reduced raw material, energy and utility requirements;
- reduced risks from handling hazardous materials and hence improved health and safety for employees;
- reduced risks for the environment, manifested by the reduction or elimination of liability charges;
- reduced risk of breaching authorization, consent or licence conditions and hence reduced risk of prosecution;
- improved operating efficiency and process reliability;
- improved company image in the eyes of shareholders, employees and the community.

Waste minimization projects do not inevitably bring about benefits for occupational health and safety. If the initial generation of waste is reduced then clearly the risks arising from it will almost certainly be reduced. On the other hand, if the same amount of waste is being better managed (so that less has to leave the process environment) then a greater number of personnel could become exposed to the dangers from the waste. In this case careful attention needs to be given to their health and safety needs if there is to be no reduction in standards.

In the economic evaluation phase of a waste minimization programme, it is important that all potential benefits are correctly appraised and quantified. And it may be difficult to quantify some of the potential benefits.

3. COMPANY AND MANAGEMENT COMMITMENT

It is essential to the success of waste minimization programmes that the most senior management within a company take a leading role. This is to ensure that there is:

- a declared company policy and a strategy for its implementation;
- a managerial commitment;
- provision of adequate resources;
- an adequate mechanism for the allocation of true waste management costs to the source of waste generation;
- a programme for personnel training;
- strong encouragement for the implementation of waste minimization projects.

It is important for process engineers engaged in waste minimization activities to know and understand their company's policy and how it allocates its waste disposal costs.

3.1 COMPANY POLICY AND IMPLEMENTATION

3.1.1 COMPANY POLICY

A company should be committed to waste minimization. Its overall objectives and strategies, and timescales for their achievement, should be defined in the organizational plan for the implementation of its environmental management system — for example, the British Standard on Environmental Management Systems[8] and the European Community Eco-Management and Audit Regulation.

3.1.2 IMPLEMENTATION

The proactive commitment of senior management is essential to the success of a waste minimization programme. The commitment is required to make the difference between simply preparing an overall objective, such as that given in the company's policy statement, and preparing a specific plan which can be successfully implemented, audited and reviewed. A senior manager may be allocated the responsibility for the waste minimization programme.

3.1.3 ADEQUATE RESOURCE ALLOCATION

Not all waste minimization projects require capital investment. Indeed some initial projects are likely to involve only procedural changes or good housekeeping. Nevertheless, resources must be identified at the start of a company's waste minimization programme. Initial costs are related mostly to the need to devote man-hours to the planning, assessment and evaluation stages. Small teams of experts are needed to carry out these functions.

A waste minimization programme is concerned with creating financial savings as well as environmental protection, and it must be presumed that no individual project would be considered worthwhile unless deemed to be 'profitable'. In this respect, it has to be acknowledged that allowances may need to be made in the economic evaluation for some of the less tangible benefits which can accrue from reducing waste generation.

3.1.4 WASTE MINIMIZATION CLUBS

Companies may decide to be involved in a formal co-operative waste minimization activity. These 'clubs' are normally organized regionally and comprise a number of companies in a range of manufacturing or service activities. The best known clubs are The Aire and Calder Project[9] and Project Catalyst[10, 11].

3.2 ALLOCATION OF WASTE DISPOSAL COSTS

For a waste minimization programme to be successful, it is clearly necessary for a policy on the appropriate allocation of waste management costs to be established by senior management. This may be achieved through the accountancy system in such a way as to show distributed waste management costs rather than a central and total figure. All waste management costs, including storage and transport, should be identified as waste management activities and not allocated simply in general operating overheads.

The true value of a waste minimization programme, and of its individual projects, becomes more visible to both senior management and site personnel if all the true costs which are associated with waste are allocated to the source of the waste and are reflected in the products concerned. In this way the impact of waste generation on production costs is identified, and the importance of waste minimization highlighted.

If general on-site waste treatment and disposal services are still being used, allocation options may include the following:
• each operating department is allocated some portion of the fixed costs of the on-site service;

10

- each operating department is charged variable costs of treatment and disposal on the basis of the quantity/nature of the wastes;
- various operating departments are charged transfer prices for the quantities/types of wastes treated and disposed of.

3.3   BARRIERS TO BE OVERCOME

The development of an environmental protection strategy based on waste minimization represents a major shift in thinking from traditional 'end-of-pipe' pollution control practices. Inevitably there are concerns regarding risk to product quality resulting from any process change. For a waste minimization programme to be successful, it must provide environmental and/or monetary benefits through the prevention of pollution. All staff within a company should recognize that there are potential economic, technical, regulatory and in-house barriers to implementation, and attempts should be made to overcome them.

3.3.1   ECONOMIC BARRIERS

Economic barriers can occur when a company believes it does not have the financial ability or incentive to implement waste minimization. Even in such a position the company should seek to identify waste minimization projects which require low capital investment. For example, savings in waste management costs may be gained simply through improved housekeeping and inventory control practices. Specific economic barriers and some techniques for overcoming them are given in Table 1 on page 12.

3.3.2   TECHNICAL BARRIERS

Specific technical barriers and measures to overcome them are given in Table 2 on page 13.

3.3.3   REGULATORY BARRIERS

The legislative framework may appear to present barriers to waste minimization. Clearly, regulatory requirements (such as those under Part 1 of EPA 1990) can be a driving force for cleaner technology/waste minimization and not a barrier to it. However, it is not only legislation on environmental matters which is relevant. In particular, environmental needs must be reconciled with the Control of Substances Hazardous to Health (COSHH) Regulations which concern occupational health and safety. In addition, changes to processes, plants and developments on new sites may require planning applications, environmental assessments, changes to operating licences and so on. Since the main non-financial objective to waste minimization is to benefit the environment, regulatory

TABLE 1

Economic barriers to a waste minimization programme

Specific barrier	Measures to overcome barrier
Overall production cost increases: • raw material costs increase • production rate decreases • new equipment is required.	Economic evaluation must include the full and true cost of: • pollution control • waste management • potential future liabilities if no change.
Greater capital investment than for pollution control and waste treatment is required.	All the less tangible and less easily quantified benefits should be incorporated into the profitability analysis.
Costs increase or projects are not profitable even when less tangible benefits are included.	Consideration should be given to whether wastes are or may become: • particularly hazardous • particularly toxic since the continued existence of a product line may depend on the hazards associated with its production.
Waste minimization projects seem economically favourable but the required capital is unavailable.	Financial assistance should be sought.

barriers should be relatively easy to overcome by working with the appropriate regulatory bodies in the planning process.

3.3.4   CULTURAL BARRIERS

Resistance to change and friction among elements within a company may introduce barriers. Problems may be caused by:
• lack of senior management commitment and responsibility;
• lack of awareness of corporate goals and objectives;
• individual or organizational resistance to change;
• poor internal communication;
• restrictive employment practices;
• inflexible organizational structure;
• bureaucracy, particularly in the generation of cost data.

TABLE 2
Technical barriers to a waste minimization programme

Specific barrier	Measures to overcome barrier
Lack of suitable engineering information on techniques.	Company and employees need to be alert to information from: • government bodies • trade associations • professional institutions • consultants • literature both in the UK and abroad.
Concerns about changes to product quality and customer acceptance.	Company should review customer needs. Carry out pilot testing of new processes and products. Increase quality control in manufacture.
Retrofitting of process causes shutdown of existing operation.	Reduce impact by involving design and product personnel in the planning process.
New operation may not work as expected or may create a bottleneck in production.	Use well-tried technology wherever appropriate.
Production facility may not have space to accommodate easily the additional equipment.	Carry out pilot testing in the plant to reduce the impact on existing processes.
Employee reaction such as: • it has been tried before • it cannot be done.	Take feedback and re-evaluate as above in this table.

Cultural barriers can be overcome with education and training programmes and with managerial improvements. Personnel at all levels in a company should be encouraged to participate in waste minimization programmes.

3.4   EMPLOYEE TRAINING AND MOTIVATION

A major element in the successful implementation of a waste minimization policy is the training of personnel within a company. Employees at all levels should be encouraged to provide valuable information about operational problems and insights into possible solutions. The co-operation of employees is also necessary for the implementation of waste minimization projects, particularly those which are concerned with good operating practices or good housekeeping. Thus training and motivating employees should be key features of a company's waste minimization strategy.

Example subject matter for training courses includes the following:
- company policy and managerial commitment;
- overview of legislation and regulations;
- definitions of waste types;
- descriptions of risks to health, safety and the environment from waste generation;
- definitions of waste minimization, recycling and treatment — the optimum hierarchy of waste management;
- potential for waste generation within the company;
- impact of waste generation on-site and off-site;
- benefits to be gained from waste minimization;
- barriers to be overcome and techniques for overcoming them;
- description of waste minimization techniques, including source reduction and recycling;
- waste minimization methodology, including preparation, assessment, evaluation, reporting, implementation, review and feedback;
- case studies of successful waste minimization projects.

Incentive schemes — for example, letters of commendation, lump sum awards, bonuses or shares of the savings made as a result of a new waste minimization project — can be implemented to motivate employees to suggest ideas and to achieve waste minimization targets. Company newsletters can be used to promote successful projects so that other plants or departments can identify with success.

The series of IChemE Environmental Training Packages is particularly relevant to the modern processing industry. The Waste Minimization Training Package[1] has been designed to provide multimedia interactive training particularly for process engineers.

4. METHODOLOGY OF WASTE MINIMIZATION

The methodology of waste minimization is summarized in Figure 3 on page 16. Several discrete steps or phases and feedback loops are involved.

The stepwise procedure outlined in Figure 3 is suitable for all process engineering companies, although it can be tailored to meet local needs. For example, a small company may be able to dispense with the steps concerned with the preliminary ranking of options and the implementation of lower priority projects, since its waste generation activities might only warrant the implementation of one or two projects.

4.1 SETTING GOALS AND TIMESCALES

The first step in a waste minimization programme is to set realistic goals and timescales that are consistent with the policy adopted by company management. Qualitative goals such as 'a significant reduction in the quantity of substances to be released into the environment' are too vague. Quantitative goals and timescales, although more difficult to establish, not only communicate the company's commitment to waste minimization better, but also provide a basis for measuring progress. Examples might be:
- to reduce wastes and emissions on a polyethylene plant by 55% by the year 2000;
- to reduce wastes and emissions on a polyethylene plant by 10% per annum.
        Quantitative goals should be:
- sufficiently flexible and adaptable to account for conditions encountered in actual practice;
- reviewed and refined periodically, based not only on lessons learned but also on the receipt of new information and understanding;
- useful and meaningful for plant personnel;
- clearly defined in terms understood by the personnel responsible for their implementation;
- challenging enough to motivate staff but not unreasonable or impractical.
        The size of the employee group required to develop the goals depends on the size and complexity of the establishment. However, it is essential that senior management is involved in the process.

4.2   THE ASSESSMENT AND EVALUATION TEAM

Waste minimization assessment and evaluation affects many functional groups within a company. Good organization is therefore required because close co-operation between groups is essential to the success of the programme. A small assessment and evaluation team should be drawn from personnel with direct

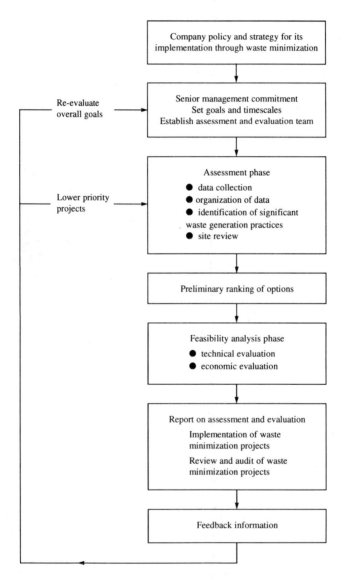

Figure 3   Methodology of waste minimization.

responsibility and knowledge of the waste streams and areas of the plant under consideration, and could include a plant operator at or below supervisor level. The team should report directly to senior management. Specialists can be consulted or co-opted when necessary, but the areas of expertise that should be considered for inclusion in the assessment and evaluation team include those in Table 3 on page 18.

The assessment and evaluation team leader should:
- be a senior member of staff;
- be selected by management or with management support to communicate clearly the organization's commitment to the assessment;
- have a strong commitment to waste minimization;
- be knowledgeable about the process and plant;
- be able to plan and to manage;
- be able to work well with the full range of personnel involved.

In order to act as a catalyst and to counter preconceived ideas held by plant personnel, it can be helpful to include at least one team member from outside the plant under consideration. This 'external' member could either be a consultant or a senior employee, with experience of waste minimization, from another part of the company's operation.

In addition, it is particularly important that there is a good understanding of process chemistry and chemical engineering, especially of the influence of process conditions on the generation of waste or off-specification materials. Not only is it important to explore the mechanisms by which unwanted contaminants may be produced, but also the kinetics with which such mechanisms operate relative to the desired mechanisms. Such an understanding may help to reduce the often significant quantities of waste generated at start-up and shutdown.

4.3   ASSESSMENT PHASE

For each plant under consideration, a waste minimization data gathering exercise is required. This includes a site inspection or review, and helps to understand the process plant or system, and hence to identify and characterize all waste streams.

During the assessment phase (sometimes called the audit phase), the assessment and evaluation team must:
- determine the root causes of waste and rank them by size, economic value, hazard, etc;
- determine the sources, quantities, compositions and hazard properties of wastes being generated, including variations in these characteristics with stages

TABLE 3
Expertise for inclusion in the assessment and evaluation team

Expertise	Function
Management	Demonstrate commitment visually and financially Authorize resources
Environmental	Provide information on: • regulations • pollution control • waste disposal costs • hazards and risks
Quality assurance and quality control	Provide information on: • current performance • specification constraints
Design and process engineering	Provide information on: • plant • current processes Quantify impacts of changes
Production and maintenance	Provide: • descriptions of plant • descriptions of processes • feedback on proposed changes
Legal	Evaluate and interpret potential environmental liability
Accounting, finance and purchasing	Provide information on: • costs • inventory controls
Health and safety	Provide data on costs, hazards and risks
Research and development	Suggest modifications Generate options
Operators, supervisors and transport department	Provide suggestions Help assess operational, procedural or equipment changes
External consultants	Question established procedures

in the production process such as batch processing, grade or product changes, start-up, shutdown, etc;
- determine how these characteristics vary with time, particularly outside the period of the assessment;
- identify how the waste streams are currently being disposed of, including:
— emissions to the atmosphere (controlled and fugitive);
— liquid discharges to sewer;
— disposal to land;
— solids, sludge and liquid wastes transported off-site;
- determine the true current costs of handling, storing, treating, transporting and disposing of wastes;
- identify situations where raw materials, products or recyclable materials are being wasted through poor handling, poor operating conditions, etc;
- determine whether raw materials, products and wastes are lost accidentally;
- examine opportunities for recycling (use, reuse and reclamation) of waste materials;
- determine what (if any) waste minimization practices, such as good housekeeping, have already been implemented;
- develop a comprehensive set of new waste minimization options;
- identify options that warrant more detailed technical and economic evaluations.

A fundamental objective of creating such a waste tracking exercise (Section 4.3.1) is to develop a waste flow diagram for each plant and process which can provide a quantitative mass balance for all the inputs and outputs, including all the wastes, discharges and emissions (Section 4.3.2, page 22). The waste flow diagrams then act not only as the focus for identifying significant waste generation practices (Section 4.3.3, page 26) but also as an aide-mémoire for site reviews (Section 4.3.4, page 27).

4.3.1   DATA COLLECTION

Much of the data needed for the assessment phase may be available as part of normal plant operation or in response to existing regulatory requirements. The major sources of data are summarized in Table 4 on page 20 and include:
- environmental information;
- design information;
- raw material and production information;
- economic information;
- other information.

Clearly the extent and complexity of the data collection process should be consistent with the needs and size of the company; the goal is to minimize waste and not simply accumulate records. The information gathering exercise

TABLE 4
Information for waste minimization assessments

Environmental information	Waste manifests and disposal records
	Waste analyses, flows and concentrations
	Wastewater discharge records and analyses
	Air emission records and analyses
	Compliance requirements
	Air emission limits
	Discharge consents
	Site licence controls
	Environmental assessment reports
	BS environmental management system, preparatory review
	Environmental audit reports
	Environmental health office data
Design information	Process descriptions
	Process flow diagrams
	Design and actual material and energy balances for production and pollution control processes
	Operating manuals
	Equipment lists, specifications and data sheets
	Piping and instrumentation diagrams
	Plot and elevation plans
	Equipment layouts and work flow diagrams
Raw materials and production information	Raw materials, product and intermediate specifications
	Material safety and environmental data sheets
	COSHH assessments
	Product and raw material inventory records
	Operator data logs and day books
	Operating procedures
	Production schedules
Economic information	Treatment and disposal costs for all forms of waste
	Water and sewer charges
	Product, utility, energy and raw material costs
	Operating and maintenance costs
	Departmental cost accounting reports
	Storage and transport costs
Other information	Company environmental policy statements
	Standard procedures
	Organizational charts
	Planning consents and conditions
	Personnel policy

should focus particularly on:
• obtaining a good inventory of waste streams;
• identifying the sources of waste streams;
• quantifying the true costs of pollution control, treatment, waste storage and disposal.

Most companies need to move towards integrated approaches to pollution prevention that cover air, water, solid waste emissions and releases. Changes which must be anticipated in the Special Waste Regulations of the Control of Pollution Act 1974 include the need to provide more detailed information on consignment notes, not only on quantities but also on the analyses of wastes. Whilst these changes will automatically increase the amount of data on quantities and compositions, the specific sources and the time periods during which the wastes were generated also need to be documented. This is especially important for the unsteady-state phases of production such as start-up, shutdown and batch processing. Identification of the time periods when waste or off-specification material is produced helps the assessment and evaluation team to focus its attention on the most critical parts of the overall operation.

The need to comply with legal requirements provides further data. For example:
• if large quantities of Special Waste are stored on site prior to, or during, treatment, then a Waste Management licence may be required — the licence would set controls which the assessment and evaluation team should be aware of;
• the COSHH Regulations 1988 lay down requirements for assessment of risk and the effective implementation and management of precautionary measures — the assessments should provide useful environmental and hazard data;
• the National Rivers Authority and Her Majesty's Inspectorate of Pollution set consents and discharge levels — the required programmes of sampling and analysis of effluents provide data for the waste minimization assessment.

Information in the plant design manual and data collected during normal and abnormal plant operations provide further and sometimes more useful data than that recorded under legislative requirements. For example, operating manuals and procedures define how a process is actually operated. Data so collected can provide specific information on all streams entering, leaving and within the process, and how events may change with time.

Whilst the generation of waste may be easiest to recognize in the production environment, there are other areas within a company from which valuable information may also be obtained. These include:
• inventory control;
• purchasing;
• records and archives;

- accounts;
- marketing and sales.

Indeed, inventory and purchasing departments themselves may be able to provide waste minimization opportunities. For example, extra stock and an unnecessary diversity of materials can lead to safety and waste problems. Also material bought in quantity at a lower unit price may not be cost-effective in the long term if unused materials need to be discarded later.

The data base should be kept up to date, since it will be required for the subsequent review and modification phases (see Sections 4.8 and 4.9 on pages 35 and 37).

4.3.2 ORGANIZATION OF DATA (THE WASTE FLOW DIAGRAM)

The process flow diagram is the foundation for preparing material and energy balances. Such diagrams can be conveniently used to identify visually and to record where, how and when wastes are generated. A waste flow diagram[32] can be used to record raw material usage, production rates, utility usage, waste stream flow rates and compositions, including effluents to treatment plants, to sewer, emissions to air, planned and fugitive; even temporal variations can be recorded.

The preparation of a waste flow diagram clearly requires a knowledge of process engineering and the chemical and physical properties of all inputs and outputs, as well as the flow characteristics of the system under study. It is therefore most appropriate for the assessment and evaluation team to include at least one experienced chemical engineer. Within each plant or process under study it is necessary to track materials as they change from raw materials and utility inputs to products, by-products, wastes, discharges and emissions. Tracking must start from the procurement of materials to off-site waste management (Figure 4) so that all known sources, quantities and characteristics of all wastes can be recorded, and the waste flow diagram can be designed.

A conceptual waste flow diagram is shown in Figure 5 on page 24. Materials balances, total material and component are applicable to the whole of the waste flow diagram, as well as to individual parts of it. All flow rates, compositions and so on of all streams should be included.

The assessment and evaluation team needs to take care when applying a mass balance boundary to such a diagram. For example, plants designed to operate at steady-state rarely achieve this condition in practice without sophisticated control. In addition, the emptying and filling of feed, product and intermediate storage tanks are unsteady-state operations which may need to be taken into account in the material balances. The importance of storage tanks should not be underestimated, since it is common practice in some plants to record flow rates from tank dips rather than rely on installed flowmeters.

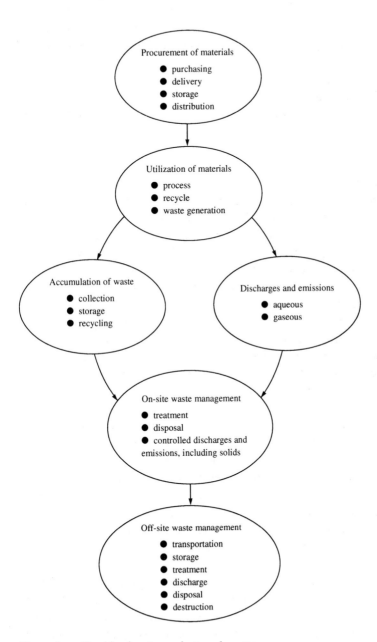

Figure 4   Tracking inputs, products and wastes.

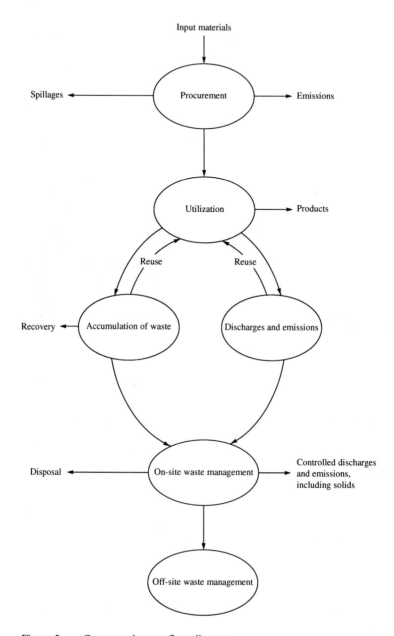

Figure 5   Conceptual waste flow diagram.

For plants designed to operate in batch or semi-batch mode it is necessary to include accumulation terms in the material and energy balances. In such cases, periods of time over which the balances are made must be defined so that the critical periods during which wastes are being generated can be identified.

Fundamentally, the mass of material entering a system boundary should equal the mass of material leaving the system, having made due allowance for accumulation. In practice, however, the difficulty of establishing waste flows from differences in two or more major flows should be recognized. Failure to close a material balance indicates the presence of one or both of the following:

• a problem with the accurate determination of plant data, including flow rates and compositions;

• unmeasured releases or inputs which need to be identified and quantified.

If the plant instrumentation is accurate, then the material balances can possibly be used to estimate the concentrations of waste constituents where quantitative composition data are limited. This may be particularly useful if there are points in the production process where it is difficult or uneconomical to collect or analyse samples. Unfortunately a small error in either flow rate or composition determination — when applied over a long timespan of a high rate of production, say, one year — could mislead the assessment and evaluation team into believing that fugitive emissions or discharges are significant in quantity. Even worse, small errors could make it seem that extraneous material had been gained by the process. It is important therefore that:

• the assessment team is aware of the accuracy of all plant data;

• all methods of measurement are of the highest accuracy and are well maintained and regularly calibrated.

Use of a controlled production run might help the team identify the causes of errors and uncertainties. But in any case, the assessment team must be sufficiently experienced to recognize that in almost every case the balance diagrams will be incomplete, approximate or both.

Specific difficulties include:

• most modern processes are complex and have numerous process streams, many of which can interact with the various environmental media;

• the exact composition of many streams is unknown and cannot easily be established;

• plant stream sampling may not be easy or accurate, particularly when solids are involved;

• phase changes occur within the process, requiring multimedia analysis and correlation;

• plant operations or product mixtures change frequently, so that the material

and energy flows cannot be characterized by a single balance diagram;
- many plants lack sufficient historical data to characterize all streams.

4.3.3   IDENTIFICATION AND RANKING OF SIGNIFICANT WASTE STREAMS

The waste minimization assessment and evaluation team should target plants, processes, operations or waste streams for study and preparation of flow sheets. Ideally all waste streams and plant operations are assessed. For large, complex sites or when resources are limited, however, some form of prioritization is required. Obviously the assessments should concentrate initially on the most important waste problems, perhaps those dealing with the largest quantities of the most hazardous materials. Processes which deal with chemicals on the 'Red List' (Table 5) may deserve early attention. Then, as resources permit, assessments of lower priority problems can be made. Use the waste minimization goals set in the planning stage (Section 4.1, page 15) to guide the selection of areas to be assessed first. Typical factors to be taken into consideration include:
- compliance with current and anticipated regulations;
- costs of waste management, including pollution control, treatment and waste disposal;

TABLE 5
Chemicals on the UK 'Red List'

Under integrated pollution control (IPC), Her Majesty's Inspectorate of Pollution (HMIP) is responsible for authorizing discharges of liquid effluents from certain prescribed processes and substances (as defined in the Environmental Protection (Prescribed Processes and Substances) Regulations 1991 (SI 1991/472). For discharges into waters, prescribed substances are as follows:

- mercury and its compounds
- cadmium and its compounds
- all isomers of hexachlorocyclohexane
- all isomers of DDT
- pentachlorophenol and its compounds
- hexachlorobenzene
- hexachlorobutadiene
- aldrin
- dieldrin
- endrin
- polychlorinated biphenyls
- dichlorvos

- 1,2–dichloroethane
- all isomers of trichlorobenzene
- atrazine
- simazine
- tributyltin compounds
- triphenyltin compounds
- trifluralin
- fenitrothion
- azinphos-methyl
- malathion
- endosulfan

- potential environmental and safety liability (inevitably linking into COSHH, CIMAH, Hazop and Hazan studies);
- quantities of waste;
- hazardous properties of the waste, including toxicity, flammability, corrosivity and reactivity;
- other hazards to employees;
- potential for waste reduction;
- potential for reduction in raw material usage;
- potential for reduction in energy and utilities usage;
- potential for removing bottlenecks in production or waste treatment;
- potential recovery of valuable by-products;
- budget available for the waste minimization assessment programme and ensuing projects.

4.3.4   SITE REVIEW

Once a specific plant, process, operation or waste stream has been selected, the assessment phase continues with a site review. Here are some guidelines for carrying out the site review:

- prepare in advance an agenda which covers all aspects requiring clarification. Distribute the agenda to all relevant personnel in the area being studied, in advance of the site inspection;
- schedule the site inspection to coincide with operations specifically related to waste generation — for example, start-up, shutdown, product change;
- monitor the operation at different times during the shift and, if necessary, during several shifts, especially when waste generation is highly dependent on human involvement;
- investigate maintenance procedures during normal operation and during shutdown;
- interview operators, shift supervisors and foremen in the area being inspected. Take note of their familiarity with the impacts that their operation may have on other operations;
- photograph the area being inspected for future reference;
- observe the housekeeping. Check for spills and leaks, odours and fumes, and assess the overall site cleanliness. Visit the maintenance workshop to identify particular difficulties in keeping equipment free from leaks;
- assess the organizational structure and level of co-ordination of environmental activities between various departments;
- assess administrative procedures such as cost accounting, material purchasing and waste collection.

27

Even if the entire assessment and evaluation team is employed at the site being assessed, the site review is still valuable in providing the team with a systems perspective of the entire situation. Site personnel will, of course, be familiar with their own areas of responsibility. However, they may see the plant or process in a new light when involved in a waste minimization assessment. For example, actual operations will be witnessed and thus modifications made to equipment and procedures can be checked against the most up-to-date flow diagrams and equipment lists.

The site review is even more important if there are external personnel on the assessment and evaluation team. In this case an opportunity is created for the outside personnel (either company personnel not associated with the site under review or consultants external to the company) to provide a fresh perspective.

In the site inspection, the assessment and evaluation team tracks the process from the points where raw materials enter the area under review to the points where all the products and all the wastes leave. The team identifies all suspected sources of waste, including:

- the production process;
- piping;
- maintenance operations;
- storage areas for raw materials, products, work in progress and wastes.

The inspection results in the formation of preliminary conclusions about the causes of waste generation. Confirmation of the preliminary conclusions may require:

- additional data collection;
- additional data analysis;
- further site visits.

Ensure that field notes on the site inspection are carefully completed — they can be used to create a formal record which can be referred to later on in the reviewing and auditing phases.

4.4 PRELIMINARY RANKING OF PRACTICAL WASTE MINIMIZATION OPTIONS

Having completed the assessment phase, the next stage is to carry out a preliminary screening exercise to identify candidates for more detailed technical and economic evaluations. Screening is necessary because detailed technical and economic feasibility exercises can be expensive. The objective is to place waste minimization options into priority groups in order to guide the allocation of resources for the detailed feasibility analyses.

Source reduction techniques are considered to be good operating practices since they avoid or minimize the generation of waste. Thus options which fall into this category should be placed in the highest priority group.

Recycling techniques, either on-site or off-site, allow waste materials to be put to beneficial use. But recycling techniques do not avoid the generation of waste, so they should not be ranked alongside source reduction techniques.

Treatment options should be considered only if acceptable source reduction and recycling options cannot be identified.

The screening procedure will therefore eliminate options that appear impractical, inferior or otherwise of marginal value.

Several problem-solving techniques can be used to generate ideas, analyse problems and set priorities. Brainstorming sessions with the assessment and evaluation team members are an effective way of developing the ranking of waste minimization options. The actual screening process can be carried out by an informal review and a decision made by the programme manager, or by other methods favoured by the company.

Whatever preliminary ranking method is used, the following aspects need to be considered for each option:

- what is the main benefit to be gained? Examples include economics, compliance, liability and safety;
- what other benefits will be gained?
- does the necessary technology exist to implement the option?
- is the necessary technology likely to be cost-effective?
- can implementation be carried out within a reasonable amount of time without disrupting production?
- does the option have a good track record? If not, is there convincing evidence that the option will be successful?

The ranking process should take into account the ease with which an option can be implemented. Some options — for example, those which are considered to be good housekeeping — may only require procedural changes and incur no capital investment. Implementation can therefore be quick and not require further evaluation if potential cost savings have been identified.

Make a formal record of the preliminary ranking phase since it can be referred to later on in the reviewing and auditing phases, and when lower priority projects are being considered for implementation.

4.5   FEASIBILITY ANALYSIS PHASE

The number of high priority options chosen for the detailed technical and economic feasibility analyses depends upon the time, budget and resources available for such studies.

The IChemE's *Guides to Capital Cost Estimating*[12] and *Economic Evaluation of Projects*[13] give further information on the development of projects.

4.5.1   TECHNICAL EVALUATION

The objective of a technical evaluation is to determine whether a proposed waste minimization option will work in a specific application. Procedural or housekeeping changes can be implemented directly after appropriate review and training. Similarly, materials substitutions can be made quickly if there are no major production rate or product quality implications, or if equipment changes are not required.

Options which involve process and/or equipment changes are likely to be more expensive and may affect production rate and product quality. Such options require extensive study in order to ensure that they will perform successfully in the field.

Many technical criteria need to be considered at this stage. Questions to be asked include:

- is the proposed option safe?
- will product quality be improved or impaired?
- is space available in the existing facility?
- are the new equipment, materials or procedures compatible with production and operating procedures and with work flow and production rates?
- is additional labour required?
- are the necessary utilities available, or must they be installed, thereby further raising capital investment?
- how long will production be stopped in order to implement the changes?
- is special expertise required to operate or maintain the new system?
- does the vendor provide acceptable service?
- does the system create other and worse environmental problems?
- what are the possible effects on the operational methods?
- what is the effect on your surrounding operations and those of others?

An inability to satisfy all of these criteria may not present insurmountable problems but accounting for them could increase both the capital and operating costs.

Procedures to be followed in the technical evaluation include:

- reviews of the technical literature (least expensive);
- visits to see existing installations, arranged through equipment vendors and industrial contacts (relatively low cost but with the advantage of seeing technology at work);

- bench-scale or pilot-scale demonstration, perhaps using equipment on loan from vendors (most expensive) or at other facilities;
- advice from consultant groups.

All personnel groups in the operation which would be affected by the option under evaluation should be able to contribute to and review the results of the technical evaluation. This is important to ensure not only the viability but also the acceptability of the option. If, after the technical evaluation, the option appears to be infeasible or impractical, it should not be considered further.

4.5.2   ECONOMIC EVALUATION

The economic evaluation of waste minimization options is carried out using the company's preferred methods. The profitability of a project is normally estimated from a cost-benefit analysis. If a waste minimization option has no significant capital costs, then its profitability can be judged by whether or not operating costs are saved.

For an option which requires a capital investment and changes in operating cost, a more formal and detailed analysis is required. Examples include:
- pay-back period — that is, the amount of time it takes to recover the initial cash outlay;
- internal rate of return (IRR);
- net present value (NPV).

The pay-back period method is recommended for quick assessments of profitability, but if large capital expenditures are involved then use the discounted cash flow techniques of IRR or NPV. These techniques are particularly suitable for evaluating and ranking alternative options.

CAPITAL COSTS
Refer to the IChemE *Guide to Capital Cost Estimating*[12].

CHANGES IN OPERATING AND MAINTENANCE COSTS
All opportunities to save operating and maintenance costs should be quantified and included in the economic evaluation:
- reduced waste management costs including;
— lower on-site treatment costs;
— less waste storage space and hence more space for production;
— less pretreatment and packaging prior to disposal;
— reduced quantity to be treated off-site;
— lower transportation and disposal costs;
— lower administration costs;

- input material costs savings — an option that reduces waste should decrease the demand for input materials;
- insurance and liability savings — a waste minimization option may be significant enough to reduce insurance premiums and it may also reduce potential liabilities with respect to environmental and safety aspects;
- changes in costs associated with product quality — a waste minimization option may have a positive or a negative effect on product quality. If negative, additional costs for re-establishing the required purity might be required;
- changes in utility costs — implementation of a waste minimization option may either increase or decrease costs of steam, electricity, process and cooling water, plant air, inert gas, refrigeration and so on;
- changes in operating and maintenance labour — a waste minimization option may either increase or decrease labour requirements and involve:
— changes in the number of employees;
— changes in overtime requirements;
— changes in employee benefit costs;
— changes in supervisory requirements;
- changes in supplies for operation and maintenance — these may either be increased or decreased by a waste minimization option;
- changes in overhead costs — large waste minimization projects may affect a company's overheads structure;
- changes in revenues from increased or decreased production — a change in productivity on a unit will result in a change in revenues and operating costs;
- increased revenues from by-products — a waste minimization option may produce a by-product that can be:
— sold to a recycler;
— sold to another establishment as a raw material;
— used in another part of the company's production facilities;
- changes in costs associated with inventory and storage of raw materials, intermediates, products and wastes;
- consultants' charges.

ALLOWANCE FOR REDUCTION IN RISKS

A waste minimization option may reduce the magnitude of environmental and safety risks for a company. Although these risks may be identifiable, it can be difficult to quantify them, since it may be difficult to predict the nature and resulting magnitude of future problems. Quantification requires judgement and the incorporation of the viewpoints of the appropriate personnel within the company. Therefore it is important that such personnel are made aware of the risk reduction together with all the other benefits of a waste minimization option.

SENSITIVITY ANALYSES

The profitability of an option should be studied under optimistic and pessimistic assumptions. For example, consider the effects of inevitably rising waste disposal costs on profitability. Sensitivity analyses that indicate the effect of key variables on profitability are also useful.

COSTS OF COMPLIANCE WITH CONSENTS AND LEGISLATION

Waste reduction may well be required by a company in order to achieve compliance with consents and legislation. But it is generally assumed in this book that waste minimization is a technique for creating commercial advantages in addition to achieving compliance. While profitability is important in deciding whether or not to implement an option, environmental regulations may be even more important. Continued operation in violation of environmental regulations is likely to result in rising costs through fines, legal actions and possibly criminal actions. Ultimately, a plant or operation may be forced to close. Conversely, companies with a good public image for environmental compliance may find this to be an advantage when new developments require planning permission.

PERSPECTIVE

For those businesses with modest environmental problems, the entire minimization assessment and evaluation procedure outlined above can be simplified. It may be possible to introduce several obvious waste minimization options, such as good operating practices and good housekeeping, without the need to resort to extensive technical and economic evaluations. Clearly a proper perspective, which balances the size of the environmental problem against both the cost and complexity of the options and the time used for technical and economic feasibility analyses, must be maintained.

4.6   REPORT ON ASSESSMENT AND EVALUATION

The formal assessment report includes the following:
- targets or objectives set;
- regulations to be complied with;
- principal results of the assessment of options;
- technical and economic feasibility analyses of all the options studied;
- recommendations for the implementation of feasible options, including priorities;
- review of the principal assumptions made in arriving at the conclusions.

A summary should include a qualitative evaluation of tangible and intangible costs and benefits, not forgetting reduced liabilities and the prospect of improved image in the eyes of employees and public.

The details for each option include:
- the waste minimization potential;
- the maturity of the technology, with a discussion of successful applications;
- the overall economics, including the result of the sensitivity analyses;
- the required resources and how they will be obtained;
- the estimated time for installation and start-up;
- possible performance measures to allow the option to be audited and reviewed after it is implemented as a project (refer to Section 4.8.1, page 36).

Before a report is issued in its final form, it should be reviewed by affected departments in order to solicit ideas and gain support. This action increases the likelihood of projects becoming implemented. The final report should be presented to all the departments likely to be affected so that their cooperation in implementing selected projects can be gained.

4.7   IMPLEMENTATION OF WASTE MINIMIZATION PROJECTS

The assessment and evaluation report provides the basis for obtaining funding of waste minimization projects. Since projects are not always sold on their technical merits alone, the report must include a clear description of all tangible and intangible benefits.

The waste minimization assessment and evaluation team — that is, the authors of the report — should be flexible enough to develop alternatives or modifications to its conclusions if this is considered necessary by senior management. The team should also be committed to carrying out additional background and support work, and should anticipate potential problems in implementing the options.

Waste minimization projects that only involve operational, procedural or materials changes — that is, without additions and modifications to process and to equipment — should be implemented as soon as possible. For projects which involve equipment or process modifications or new equipment, the implementation of a waste minimization project is essentially no different from any other capital project, and involves planning, financial authorization, design, procurement, construction and commissioning phases.

Responsibilities and timescales for the projects to be implemented should be set by senior management, and attention paid to informing all staff who may be affected by the changes. Adequate training and supervision are required. It is particularly important that all staff feel involved in the project; appropriate incentive schemes can be implemented to foster commitment to further waste minimization projects.

If a project appears to be potentially very profitable but cannot be exploited until either a new technology is commercially developed or major operational changes are required, then help may be sought from Government assistance schemes.

In the UK, contact should be made with the Department of Trade and Industry. Financial assistance can also be obtained via the Teaching Company Scheme, if expertise appropriate to the project is available within academia.

4.8 PROGRESS REVIEW AND AUDIT OF WASTE MINIMIZATION PROJECTS

A company should make periodic reviews of its waste minimization programme and of specific projects within the overall programme. For each project, it is necessary to:

- measure progress against established goals;
- record project successes and failures to guide future assessment, evaluation and implementation cycles;
- permit managers to pursue corporate waste minimization goals effectively.

Quantitative comparisons of measured progress with the goals can help to identify which options are most effective. This, in turn, helps identify new waste minimization techniques, aids technology development, guides planning and enhances technology transfer, so that similar plants or operations within one establishment or in other companies can be compared consistently. The quantitative comparisons are also important to demonstrate to senior management that the waste minimization efforts are proceeding as planned.

Measurement of progress involves:

- selecting a quantity to track performance;
- measuring the selected quantity;
- normalizing the data, if necessary, to correct for production changes.

Whilst this might appear straightforward, many factors must be taken into account:

- the quantity selected to track performance must accurately reflect the wastes which are of interest. Parameters include volume and/or weight reduction, toxicity reduction and economic changes;
- the quantity must be measurable — as noted in Section 4.3.1 on page 19, data may come from a variety of sources;
- measuring devices may not be available for all waste streams — this is especially true with fugitive emissions which are particularly difficult to measure;
- substantial changes in waste quantities from year to year may appear to arise from changes in regulations or accounting practices;

• the waste minimization project may have shifted the waste material to another plant stream, to another environmental medium or into the product, and it may be difficult to track the pollutant and to evaluate its relative impact on pollution;
• although it is desirable to characterize and quantify accurately the amount and the hazardous nature of the waste, its 'hazardous nature' is not routinely quantified as part of process measurement.

4.8.1   MEASUREMENT OF QUANTITIES TO TRACK PERFORMANCE

A variety of measurement techniques is available, depending on the quantity used in tracking performance. It is most probable that a single measure to summarize waste minimization achievements will be applicable only to the simplest cases, if any.

Since waste minimization is concerned with creating commercial advantages, and since economic evaluations form a major part of the methodology, it is appropriate to use profitability as a measure of performance. The value of reduced waste production may be estimated, based on the volumes of waste and the costs of waste treatment and disposal. Any of the economic evaluation methods — for example, pay-back period, NPV or IRR — may be used. But although the method chosen may provide clear evidence to senior management of the economic benefits of a waste minimization programme, it does not allow a comparison to be made with the goals which have been set, unless those goals include financial criteria.

The goals are concerned with waste quantities and timescales, and thus it becomes necessary to monitor the reduction in either volume or weight of wastes and emissions. Progress of a waste minimization project can be tracked from the changes in the quantities of waste:
• transported off-site;
• treated on-site;
both before and after implementation of the project.

Waste shipments off-site should be relatively easy to track from waste manifests and consignment notes. The amount of waste going to on-site treatment plants may be more difficult to obtain but it may be possible to make reasonably accurate measurements or estimates. Fugitive emissions are much more difficult to track but it may be possible to make estimates of these quantities from material balances.

Progress of a waste minimization project can also be tracked from the change in quantity of waste generated or used. This quantity-based measurement compares the amounts of waste materials generated and/or used on site. The quantities of hazardous, toxic and other waste material flows into and out of the facility are tracked, including:

- material purchase;
- production and destruction in the process;
- incorporation in products and by-products;
- discharges to waste or treatment.

The method is essentially an overall material balance on each waste component and requires extensive data collection.

Waste minimization can be tracked by the change in the total amounts and the toxicity of materials released. Clearly this method requires ways of determining both the quantities and the relative toxicities of waste streams. Suitable sampling and analytical facilities must be established. The level of sophistication, and hence expense, may not be appropriate to many plants.

4.8.2   NORMALIZING THE DATA

In plants where production rates change or the type of product or range of products alters, it is necessary to standardize or normalize the measures used to track progress. Possible normalizing factors include:

- hours of process operation;
- hours of employee work;
- area, weight or volume of product made;
- number of batches processed;
- area, weight or volume of raw material purchased;
- revenue from product;
- profit from product.

No single factor will apply to all plants, and each has its advantages and disadvantages:

- product output or raw material input rates can be good for continuous processes;
- total production volume or raw material use can be good for batch processes, although the coupling may be weak or not in direct proportion;
- monetary factors typically apply only to stable markets — revenues and profits may indicate the amount of activity but may not be reliable indicators if price changes occur due to market forces;
- some waste stream rates may vary inversely with the production rate — for example, a waste resulting from outdated input materials is likely to increase if the production rate decreases.

4.9   FEEDBACK OF INFORMATION

Maintenance of a waste minimization programme requires a feedback process to be implemented. The feedback process should collect sufficient data and information at intervals consistent with the size and complexity of the company. Feedback should be sufficiently frequent and detailed to provide employees with enough information to identify the accomplishments and the status of current activities.

Feedback is also important because the conditions surrounding waste minimization are dynamic. For example:

- research and development may reveal new opportunities;
- new technologies may become available at attractive costs;
- economic conditions may change, particularly those relating to waste disposal methods;
- legislation may change so that some waste disposal methods become prohibited and others favoured;
- society's attitudes may change.

Review of a waste minimization programme is especially required when major changes are being made to plants and processes for other commercial reasons.

4.10   IMPLEMENTATION OF LOWER PRIORITY PROJECTS

The ultimate goal of a waste minimization programme is to reduce the generation of waste to the lowest possible amount. So a waste minimization programme should be ongoing rather than a one-off project. Once the highest priority options have been assessed and evaluated, and the projects have been implemented, attention can then be paid to options originally deemed to be of medium or low priority.

Initial attention may have been paid to reducing the amounts of the most voluminous or the most toxic wastes, but ultimately attention needs to turn to reducing all industrial wastes, and emissions to air, water and land.

4.11   RE-EVALUATION OF OVERALL GOALS

From time to time, the programme should be reviewed to take into account:

- changes in raw material or product requirements;
- increased waste management costs;
- new regulations;
- new technology;
- major events with undesirable environmental consequences — for example, major spills.

These factors may require periodic reviews of overall goals and company policy.

Maintaining a waste minimization programme is as important as starting one, and one of the most effective ways of keeping momentum is to ensure that decision-makers are charged with the full cost of waste disposal for the units under their control. If possible, these costs should include those for liability and compliance. It is unacceptable to hide the costs of waste management in the general overheads, since the illusion is created that waste disposal is effectively free for the plant unit in question.

5. PRACTICAL TECHNIQUES TO MINIMIZE WASTE

An overall summary of practical minimization techniques which can be applied to waste generation problems is shown in Figure 6. The techniques fall into two broad categories — reduction of waste at source and recycling. In principle, the former is preferable to the latter because the use of recycling infers that process plants, raw material flows and utility consumptions will be higher than if no recycle were necessary. In practice, however, there are many factors — thermodynamic, kinetic and so on — which mean that most waste minimization strategies involve some form of recycling, often in combination with reduction of waste at source and with changes to waste treatment practice.

Techniques for the reduction of waste at source can be divided into four broad categories, as shown in Figure 6. Changes to technology can be further divided into waste minimization on existing processes — that is, retrofitting — and the design of cleaner processes. Clearly on large and complex processes, combinations of retrofitting and new technology are most likely.

Examples of practical techniques are provided in References 1–5 and 14–19. To illustrate a particular area, Chapter 8 gives a list, taken from the US EPA Draft Guide[3], of waste minimization options which are particularly appropriate to solvent cleaning operations.

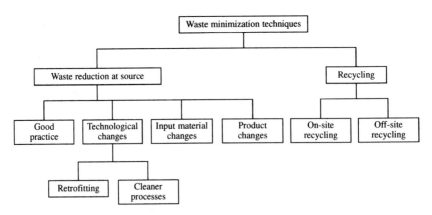

Figure 6   Practical techniques for waste minimization.

Case Study 1

The UK Department of Trade and Industry's (DTI's) first business guide to *Cutting Your Losses*[4] describes the approach that Allied Colloids took to deal with the waste from a liquid dispersion polymers (LDP) process. The waste mixed with water formed a viscous sludge which was difficult to treat and dispose of. In 1984 a settlement tank was installed to extract waste LDPs and solvent before coming into contact with large volumes of waste water. The waste polymers and solvent could then be skimmed off from the waste water and distilled. Waste LDP was unusable but the recovered solvent (5 tonnes per week of white spirit) could be reused.

Having extracted the white spirit, LDP waste could be landfilled at a cost of £100 per tonne; the only previous alternative was incineration at a cost of £500 per tonne. In addition, LDP waste was reduced in volume from 20 to 10 tonnes per week because the LDP was recovered before it could absorb water.

At 1989 prices, the additional plant would cost about £25,000 and be operated and maintained by one employee. Weekly disposal costs were reduced from £10,000 to £1000 and an additional saving of £1000 per week was made on the purchase of white spirit. The pay-back on the investment was less than three weeks.

This example shows that it is sometimes necessary to combine waste reduction at source and recycling (in this case of the solvent) and take advantage of lower cost disposal routes in order to obtain an impressive pay-back.

5.1 REDUCTION OF WASTE AT SOURCE

Methods for reduction of waste at source fall into several categories, including those which deal with how the product is made and those which deal with the composition and/or use of the product. There is no preferred hierarchy to the categories.

5.1.1 GOOD PRACTICE

Attention to good operating practice, good housekeeping, good engineering and maintenance which involves operational improvements or administrative changes can often be implemented relatively quickly to reduce waste. This reduces costs without incurring significant investment. Pay-back may be as short as a few days. Examples include:

- clear specification of good housekeeping and materials handling procedures;
- implementing Quality Assurance techniques;
- regular auditing of materials purchased against materials used;
- avoidance of over-ordering;

- regular preventive maintenance;
- segregation of waste streams to avoid cross-contamination of hazardous and non-hazardous materials, and to increase recoverability;
- reduction in the volume of wastes by filtration, membrane processes, vaporization, drying and compaction;
- fitting lids and vapour traps to solvent tanks;
- elimination of poor storage conditions;
- improvement of maintenance scheduling, record-keeping and procedures to increase efficiency;
- re-evaluation of shelf-life characteristics to avoid unnecessary disposal of long-life materials;
- improvement of inventory and management control procedures;
- changes from small volume containers to bulk or reusable containers;
- introduction of employee training and motivation schemes for waste reduction;
- collection of spilled or leaked material for reuse;
- consolidation of types of chemicals to reduce quantities and types of wastes (care and advice must be taken to ensure that dangers are not introduced);
- rescheduling of production to reduce frequency and number of equipment cleaning operations.

It is important that proper attention be given to eliminating or minimizing spills, leaks and contamination during the storage of raw materials, products and process wastes, and the transfer of these materials within the production facility. Examples requiring attention include:

- leaking valves, hoses, pipes and pumps;
- leaking tanks and containers;
- overfilling of tanks; inadequate, poorly maintained or malfunctioning high level protection;
- leaks and spills during material transfer;
- inadequate bunding;
- leaking filters, bunkers and bins in powder transfer operations;
- equipment and tank cleaning operations;
- contamination to produce off-specification raw materials and products by inadequate process control or by the entry of adulterating substances;
- lack of regular maintenance, inspection and operator training;
- correct sequencing of valve operations.

5.1.2 TECHNOLOGICAL CHANGES

Technology changes concern process and equipment modifications in order to reduce waste primarily within the production environment. The modifications may involve the use of new or modified processes and hardware to lessen or prevent pollution. Examples include:

- introduction of new processes or equipment which produce less waste — that is, 'clean' technologies;
- fundamental change to or better control of process operating conditions such as flow rate, temperature, pressure, residence time and stoichiometry to reduce waste and consume less raw materials and energy;
- redesign of equipment and piping to reduce the amount of material to be disposed of during start-ups, shutdowns, product changes and maintenance programmes;
- installation of vapour recovery systems to return emissions to the process;
- changes to mechanical cleaning to avoid the use of solvents and the generation of dilute liquid wastes, provided such changes are not detrimental;
- use of more efficient motors and speed control systems to reduce energy consumption.

A series of articles in *The Chemical Engineer* by Smith and Petela[14–18] provide an insight into studying ways of minimizing waste in the areas of reaction engineering, separations and recycle, process operations and utilities. In addition, interactive case studies are provided in the IChemE Waste Minimization Training Package[1].

The IChemE training package describes how basic chemical engineering knowledge can be applied to waste minimization. Two classes of waste are identified. The reaction and separation/recycle systems produce process waste such as by-products and purges. Utility waste comprises the products of fuel combustion, waste from boiler feed treatment, boiler blowdown, etc. Design of the utility system is closely tied to the heat exchanger network.

The reactor can be considered to be at the heart of most chemical engineering processes. There are five major sources of waste production from reactors:

(1) impracticality of recycling unreacted feed material back to the reactor inlet;
(2) primary reactions producing waste by-products;
(3) secondary reactions of the desired product leading to waste by-products;
(4) impurities in the feed becoming wastes or undergoing reactions to produce additional waste by-products; and
(5) degradation of catalysts or the need to replace catalysts in such a way that they have to be disposed of.

Smith and Petela's articles in *The Chemical Engineer*[14–18] and the IChemE Waste Minimization Training Package[1] then describe how to:

- reduce waste from single reactions, including waste by-product formation from single reactions, and increasing the conversion for single irreversible and reversible reactions;

- reduce waste from multiple reaction systems which produce by-products, including study of reactor types, systems of parallel and series reactions, reactor conversion, concentration, temperature, pressure and catalysts;
- reduce waste from feed impurities which undergo reaction;
- reduce waste from catalyst loss.

Following study of the reaction system, the approach adopted by the IChemE Waste Minimization Training Package[1] and the Smith and Petela articles[14–18] then turns to in-process separation and recycle. Consideration is given to:

- recycling waste streams directly;
- feed purification;
- elimination of extraneous materials for separation;
- additional separation and recycling;

Waste arising from utility systems is then considered, including:

- utility streams as sources of waste;
- energy efficiency of the process;
- local and global emissions;
- combined heat and power;
- fuel switching;
- emissions of SOx;
- emissions of NOx;
- waste from steam systems;
- waste from cooling systems.

Case Study 2

Paper mills use large quantities of water. The DTI's second business guide to *Cutting Your Losses*[5] describes the progress made at the Buckland Paper Mill operated by Arjo Wiggins. The company decided to improve the accuracy of the mass balance, drain losses and water consumption records before looking at ways in which water consumption could be reduced. Process changes and modifications made to the plant had the additional requirement of reducing drain losses and water consumption wherever possible. Savings were made through the replacement of water lines, recycling of cooling water, installation of backwater tanks, chemical changes to improve retention and improvements to process control and operational procedures.

Specific water consumption was reduced by 77%, equivalent to £400,000 per year in effluent charges at 1992 prices. The reduction in drain losses resulted in savings of £550,000 per year. As with Case Study 1 (page 41), a number of waste minimization techniques were used to effect the savings, namely good engineering, technological changes and recycling.

5.1.3 INPUT MATERIAL CHANGES

Hazardous materials used in a production process — for example, raw materials, solvents, catalyst supports, etc — may be replaceable by less hazardous or even non-hazardous materials. It is not always the case, however, that substances less hazardous to the environment are also less hazardous to those working with them. Changes in input materials may also lead to a reduction in, or avoidance of, the formation of hazardous substances. The objective should also include a reduction in the quantity of waste generated. Examples include:

- replacement of chlorinated solvents in cleaning and degreasing operations by non-chlorinated solvents, water or alkaline solutions;
- substitution of chemical biocides by alteratives, such as ozone;
- replacement of solvent-based paint, ink and adhesive formulations with water-based materials;
- substitution of a more durable coating to increase coating life;
- increase in the purity of purchased raw materials to eliminate the use of trace quantities of hazardous impurities;
- reduction of phosphorus in wastewater by reduction in use of phosphate-containing chemicals;
- replacement of hexavalent chromium salts by trivalent chromium salts in plating applications;
- replacement of solvent-based developing system by a water-based system in the manufacture of printed circuit-board;
- replacement of cyanide plating baths with less toxic alternatives.

One possible problem with material changes is that they may have an adverse effect on the production process, product quality and waste generation. For example, changing from a solvent-based to a water-based product might increase wastewater volumes and concentrations, leading to increased wastewater treatment and sludge disposal costs. Changes to health and safety also need to be considered. Clearly all the possible impacts of a proposed change must be evaluated.

Case Study 3

The United Nations Environment Programme document *Cleaner Production Worldwide*[19] describes the minimization of organic solvents in degreasing and painting. Thorn Järnkonst (Sweden) produces light fittings from aluminium or steel sheets. Metal working, degreasing and painting are the main activities. In the past degreasing was carried out using the volatile organic compound trichloroethylene which is recognized as an environmental hazard. The painting plant consisted of an automated lacquer line with different solvents being used with different colours. Air pollution within and beyond the plant was considered to be a major problem.

The move towards cleaner production was initiated by a planned increase in production, and an audit of material flows in the degreasing plant was carried out. With better housekeeping it was estimated that the need for trichloroethylene could be reduced by 50%, but in reality its use was reduced to zero by switching to biodegradable cutting oils which then allowed an alkaline degreasing operation to be used. The alkaline degrease cost $25,200 less per year than the trichloroethylene degrease and did not require the installation of recovery equipment.

In addition, the change to electrostatic powder painting using polymer-based paints has allowed a reduction in the use of solvents. Only 5% of the colours have organic solvents and are used only for the painting of short production runs in special colours or for retouching. The powder painting techniques resulted in a number of annual cost savings in solvent-based painting, including $206,000 for paint, $62,000 for cleaning, $47,000 for disposal, $33,000 for pumping and $112,000 for labour. The capital investment was $430,000 and thus the pay-back was around 11 months.

Case Study 4
The DTI's first business guide to *Cutting Your Losses*[4] describes the approach taken by Jebron Ltd to change the type of chromium salts used in electroplating operations. For a new metal finishing plant, built in 1985, the company decided to use trivalent chromium salts rather than the more commonly used hexavalent salts because they are less toxic by a factor of ten. The specific benefits gained by the company were claimed to be as follows:

• the cost of effluent treatment was reduced. If hexavalent salts had been used the company would have had to install effluent treatment facilities to convert the chromium from its hexavalent to its trivalent form;
• the build-up of solids in effluent tanks was 97% slower than it would have been if hexavalent salts had been used;
• the use of the trivalent form permitted a safer working environment;
• trivalent chromium has a higher conductivity than the hexavalent form, thereby allowing a more dilute solution to be used (5–7 grams per litre as opposed to 200–250 grams per litre);
• trivalent chromium forms a better coating, particularly when complex shapes are plated;
• a better colour of finish can be achieved with trivalent salts.

5.1.4   PRODUCT CHANGES

Product changes are reformulations of final or intermediate products, performed by the manufacturer, in order to reduce the quantity of waste arising from its manufacture. Other objectives might include:

• a change in a product's specification in order to reduce the quantity of chemicals used;

• a modification of the composition or final form of a product to make it environmentally benign;

• changes to reduce or modify packaging.

Product reformulation is one of the more difficult waste minimization techniques and, due to the proprietary nature of product formulations, specific examples are currently scarce. Case Study 3 (page 45) provides an example of how a change in the method of painting can retain customer acceptance. A further example of a product change is the manufacture of water-based coatings for applications where solvent-based coatings were used previously. Water-based coatings offer the potential to reduce volatile organic compound emissions, to eliminate solvent waste arising from the cleaning of spray equipment and to eliminate risks of operator exposure to solvents. However, since the nature of the finished product may be different, concerns about changes to product quality and customer acceptance must be addressed.

Case Study 5

The United Nations Environment Programme report *Cleaner Production Worldwide*[19] gives an example of the change from solvent to water-based adhesives. The components of a solvent-based adhesive are normally a polymer and a resin dissolved in a suitable organic solvent. The solvent is allowed to evaporate from the solution when the adhesive film is required. Various solvents can be used which can cause problems of volatile organic compound emission, high energy usage, etc.

Blueminster Ltd, a small research-based company, has developed a water-based resin dispersion technology which can be applied to a wide range of resins that have the necessary 'tackifying' properties. These resins are free from organic solvents, proteins and starches and are compatible with most polymer dispersions in all proportions. The dispersed resins remain liquid at all practical temperatures and, when mixed with the polymer, still allow uniform adhesive films to be laid down. The water-based adhesives have a much higher solids content than the solvent-based types and less energy is needed to remove the water from the adhesive film.

Several particular advantages are claimed for water-based adhesives.

They:
- are non-toxic;
- do not pollute the atmosphere or aqueous media;
- do not require special handling and do not present a fire or explosion hazard;
- require around 0.2 to 0.33 times the drying energy of solvent-based adhesives;
- do not require special solvent recovery systems;
- can generate higher levels of adhesion through penetration of absorbent substrates, such as cellulose, and will allow more time for the precise positioning of adherents;
- are particularly suitable for food packaging.

No quantifiable economic benefits are available but the benefits are claimed to be derived mainly from the lack of use of organic solvents. Significant savings in equipment, raw materials, safety precautions and overheads are claimed.

5.2   RECYCLING

Recycling waste materials for reuse, use and reclamation may provide a cost-effective alternative to treatment and disposal in many circumstances. It should be emphasized, however, that the elimination and minimization of waste at source are the preferred options in the hierarchy of waste management practices, and recycling should only be considered if all other options for waste minimization have been exhausted. It will almost certainly be more cost-effective to minimize the amount of waste at source, since waste represents a loss of either raw materials, intermediates or products which require both time and money to manage and recover. In addition, the generation of wastes and their subsequent recycling can present a range of regulatory, health and environmental risks or liabilities.

The success of recycling depends on:
- the ability to reuse waste materials by return to the originating process as a substitute for an input material; or
- the ability to use waste material as a raw material either on-site or off-site; or
- the ability to segregate recoverable and valuable materials from a waste (reclamation).

Successful reclamation depends on the ability to segregate recoverable and valuable materials from those low value materials which must be disposed of and treated in some acceptable way. The segregated material then becomes a raw material, by-product or product in its own right, although purification processes may be required to obtain the desired specifications.

48

5.2.1   ON-SITE RECYCLING

The optimum place to recover wastes is within the production facility. The following wastes are good candidates for recycling:

- contaminated versions of process raw materials, which can be used to reduce raw material purchases and waste disposal costs. Such waste can be recovered at point of source but some purification might be required;
- lightly contaminated wastes which can be used in other operations not requiring high purity materials;
- wastes which have physical and chemical properties suitable for other on-site applications — for example, the use of a caustic waste stream to neutralize an acid waste stream or the use of waste solvents, oil, etc in combustion processes;
- reuse of extracted water from dilute, high volume waste streams;
- wastes which can be refined on site, either in the main process — for example, the recycling of slop oils in an oil refinery — or in a special purpose plant — for example, a solvent refining unit.

Most on-site recycling processes themselves will inevitably generate some residue or waste which must be disposed of safely if it cannot be further used on site. The economic evaluations of on-site recovery techniques must include the cost of management and disposal of such residues. The safety and hazard aspects of storage and recycling must also be considered.

Case Study 6

Case Studies 1 and 2 (pages 41 and 44) showed that recycling can be an effective way of reducing waste when integrated with other changes. The DTI's second business guide to *Cutting Your Losses*[5] gives an example in which on-site recycling alone can be used to minimize waste and save money. Porvair plc manufactures microporous plastics which have applications in the footware and textile industries. The coating process uses laquers which are mixed in solvents. Formerly the solvent vapours were emitted into the atmosphere from the drying ovens. Now the vapours are condensed in the process by refrigeration, recovered by distillation and reused.

The plant cost £350,000 and the annual savings of around £200,000 are now used towards purchasing more expensive materials which improve the qualities of the finished products. Emissions of volatile organic compounds across the site were reduced by around 10%.

Case Study 7

The DTI's second business guide to *Cutting Your Losses*[5] also describes how a small electroplating and anodizing company, West Middlesex Plating, was able to virtually eliminate cadmium discharges by introducing a new process. This enabled rinse water to be constantly recycled and the cadmium residue to be electrolytically removed and reused. It is claimed that discharges have been totally eliminated from the previous 16,000 grams per year, thereby reducing associated water charges by £35,000 per year. Other benefits included improved rinsing from the better water quality and an extension in the interest in waste minimization to other parts of the plant. Investment in the project was £30,000 and gave a pay-back of less than four months on the savings and the retention of the cadmium plating business.

Case Study 8
Another example of how waste material can be converted into a raw material comes from the DTI's second business guide to *Cutting Your Losses*[5]. Edge trim PVC produced by Advance Tapes Ltd was found to be suitable for extrusion and granulation into a material which was suitable for reworking in various applications including moulded PVC shoes. PVC granules have been produced using existing equipment but dedicated new plant was being considered at a cost of £20,000. Reprocessing in this way saves landfill costs of £8000 per year and the reclaimed material has a value of £40,000 per year. The pay-back for a new plant would be 20 weeks.

5.2.2 OFF-SITE RECYCLING AND WASTE EXCHANGE
Wastes may be considered for use or reclamation off-site when:
- equipment is not available on site to do the job;
- not enough waste is generated to make on-site recycling cost-effective;
- the recovered material cannot be used in the production process.

Materials commonly reprocessed off-site by chemical and physical methods include oils, solvents, electroplating wastes, lead-acid batteries, scrap metal, food processing waste, plastic waste and cardboard. Some wastes have a use without the need for reprocessing or refining — for example, waste acids and alkalis.

The cost of off-site recycling depends on the purity of the waste and the market. Some materials generate revenue whilst others require payment to be taken off site for recycling. Materials for sale are expected to have a specification, to conform to the provisions of the Trade Descriptions Act and probably require a permit to transport. In a few instances waste may be transferred to another company to be used as raw material. Such an exchange can be economically advantageous to both companies, since:
- the waste management costs of the generator are reduced;
- the raw material costs of the recipient are reduced.

Due consideration must be given to the hazards associated with the wastes in transportation and to the competence of the recycling company (reference should be made to the Duty of Care of EPA 1990).

A strong commitment is required from the waste generator not only in upgrading waste materials for sale or exchange but also in finding markets.

Croner's Waste Management[6] provides a more detailed overview of the off-site recycling of chemicals, including the following aspects:

- a list of chemicals which are recyclable;
- descriptions of physical refining methods;
- information about the Chemical Recovery Association;
- assessments of economic and environmental costs and benefits;
- considerations about long-term availability of materials;
- barriers to recycling;
- establishing a contract for recycling off site;
- the role of the waste producer in off-site recycling;
- the long-term strategy of recycling;
- the use of waste as fuel;
- waste exchange.

5.3   SUPPORTING TOOLS FOR WASTE MINIMIZATION STUDIES

Several techniques involving computation, simulation, graphical construction and the use of keywords have been developed or adapted to enable process engineering waste minimization studies to be carried out efficiently at the desk. An overview of each is given here.

5.3.1   SIMULATION

Simulation of complex processes using flowsheeting packages or bespoke programs can be used to make assessments of the potential for any flowsheet to lead to the generation of waste and hence aid the study of waste minimization. A case study of the effects of choosing different reactor types and the optimization of reaction conditions on the formation of unwanted by-products in an acrylonitrile process is provided by Hopper *et al*[20].

5.3.2   HIERARCHICAL APPROACH TO PROCESS SYNTHESIS

The hierarchical decision procedure was originally developed by Douglas[21–23] for process synthesis but has been extended to include waste minimization. A design is developed from preliminary to detailed states by proceeding systematically through a series of designs in which additional details are added at each level. Some of the decisions made at each level might change the streams leaving

51

the process, and in some cases these exit streams could cause pollution problems. Hence, if the aim is to make decisions that do not result in exit streams on the flowsheet which cause adverse environmental impact, then the waste minimization goal will have been achieved. With this technique, waste generation problems can be identified as a design is developed. Alternatives can be assessed and incorporated to avoid potential pollution problems. The procedure can also be used to identify the pollution problems of existing processes.

Note that the alternatives suggested by Douglas may not always be easy to implement. In particular, changing the chemistry or seeking a new separation system will usually not be practicable for the retrofit of an existing process and may even be difficult for a new process.

Clearly the hierarchical design procedure can only be used to guide the design process qualitatively by adding more details at each level.

5.3.3   GRAPHICAL MASS BALANCE

In many processes waste materials can arise from a variety of sources including, for example, incomplete conversion of the feed, use of an impure feed and undesirable side reactions. When these sources occur simultaneously, reducing the generation of waste becomes a non-trivial task. The reactor is central to the generation of waste and so separators are often situated directly after it in order to remove various species from the product. The graphical mass balance concept developed by Flower et al[24] consists of three basic parts: the reaction box (R-box), the separation box (S-box) and the R-S box combination. The R-S box comprises the graphical mass balance. Each part consists of a diagram in which component mass flow rates are plotted against mass fractions for a specific process operation. These are used to represent the governing mass balances visually and manipulate them with the objective of reducing the waste generated.

The method lends itself to software development in which fast interactive manipulation of the mass balance becomes possible. Mass balance calculations can be made in the background and the computer screen updated as the changes are made. A case study for the production of allyl chloride is provided by Flower et al[24].

5.3.4   MASS EXCHANGE NETWORK ANALYSIS

Mass exchange network (MEN) analysis is a systematic procedure for generating a cost-effective network of mass exchangers capable of transferring certain species preferentially from a set of rich streams to a set of lean streams. A mass exchanger can be any countercurrent, direct-contact mass transfer operation that uses a mass separating agent such as a solvent or adsorbent. Common mass exchange operations include absorption, adsorption, liquid-liquid extraction, leaching and ion exchange.

There is a well-established analogy between heat and mass transfer and, in the same spirit, MEN analysis might appear to have similar features to the well-established technique of heat exchange network (HEN) analysis. It is important to stress, however, that a straightforward extension of HEN technology to MEN is not possible because of the fundamental differences between the mechanisms of transport and the equilibrium criteria in the two cases. The synthesis of MENs represents a higher dimensional problem than that of HENs, since several species are transferred and the distribution of a species between phases is dependent on the system in question. The MEN technique becomes highly mathematical for real systems. Examples of its use are provided in several publications by Bagajewicz and Masousiouthakis[25], El-Halwagi and Masousiouthakis[26, 27] and El-Halwagi and Srinivas[28].

5.3.5 ENVIRONMENTAL OPTIMIZATION (ENVOP)

The Hazop technique is a well-established method for reviewing the safety of process plant designs and their modifications. Significant modification of the Hazop technique using environmentally conditioned keywords can provide an effective way of systematically reviewing any process from the point of view of reducing the effluents that it generates. The method developed by BP and Costain, and described by Potter and Isalski[29] is based on formal review meetings. At these meetings a series of environmental objectives are set. A formal environmental optimization (Envop) review meeting follows, using appropriate keywords during which minutes of allocated actions are taken. Economic analysis is then applied to narrow down the number of options which potentially arise from the minutes. The method can in theory be applied to any chemical and/or separation process, whether new or existing. Envop can therefore be used to aid retrofitting and the design of cleaner processes.

Principal differences between Envop and Hazop are in three main areas. For Envop:
- environmental objectives are used to target the review;
- the keywords are very different;
- technical and economic analyses are included to aid the prioritization of options.

5.3.6 LIFE CYCLE ANALYSIS (LCA)

Environmental life cycle analysis or assessment (LCA), and in particular comparative LCA, is a powerful tool for reviewing the impacts that alternative products or processes have on the environment. In essence LCA is concerned with the measurement of inputs and outputs of any system whose function can be defined. It lends itself particularly to the assessment of environmental costs in the production of goods and the provision of services. For a product, LCA aims to quantify its environmental impact from the origins of the raw materials to its ultimate destiny. The technique is therefore popularly known as 'cradle to grave' analysis and clearly needs to take all processing steps into account. This is why LCA will become an important tool for the processing industries. Take, as an example, paper products. The 'cradle' is the forest from which wood pulp is obtained, and the 'grave' is probably a landfill site, or perhaps an incinerator, where the paper ultimately ends up. The paper mill is an important component in the overall scheme.

LCA is a particularly valuable tool for studying the benefits of recycling, which is one of the important techniques in waste minimization. An example — the recycling of low density polyethylene — is provided by Henstock[30].

LCA aims to quantify the environmental impact of a product from raw material procurement, through manufacturing, distribution and consumption, to ultimate disposal. A flowchart, like that shown in Figure 7, is usually drawn for each product. Comparative LCA, which seeks to assess the comparative environmental burdens of different products, addresses only those areas or issues where differences occur.

The LCA concept is relatively straightforward and basically comprises four facets:

(1) the definition of goals — that is, the purpose of the LCA;

(2) an inventory which calculates all the inputs and outputs for each activity from the cradle to the grave;

(3) an interpretation which links the inventory to the environment — that is, an impact analysis;

(4) the formulation of solutions.

The third and fourth facets are particularly challenging. Chemical engineers are familiar with the fundamental laws of physics which govern mass and energy balances. In LCA there is a need to put together what has been termed an 'ecobalance' — that is, something which combines the conservation of such resources with environmental protection. There is no fundamental law of physics to fall back on for the ecobalance, and this provides the main challenge.

Ecobalance calculations require the provision of data in five main categories: primary fuels, raw materials, deposits to land, emissions to air and emissions to water. The impacts of winning the fuels and raw materials, and of discharging wastes to land, air and water, all need to be determined and included in the LCA. Note that the word 'cycle' in LCA is inappropriate. Unlike biological

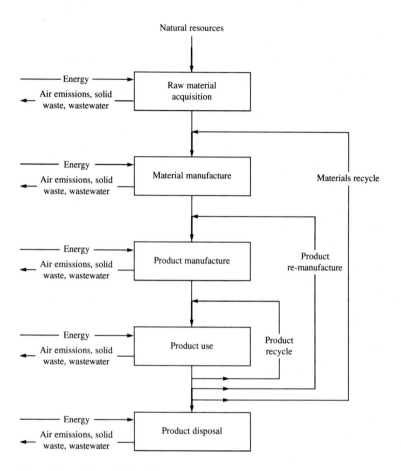

Figure 7   General LCA flowchart.

life cycles, the product in the 'grave' will rarely turn back to the raw material in the 'cradle'. The so-called cycle is therefore broken. Internal recycles are valid, however, and three forms of recycling are shown in Figure 7. The collection of milk bottles for reuse is an example of product recycle. The collection of broken glass from a recycling bin for reuse is an example of product re-manufacture. Materials recycling — that is, taking the product right back to compete with the virgin raw material — does not occur with glass. Some plastics, however, can be collected and converted into hydrocarbons suitable either as raw materials or as fuels.

So far, no mention has been made of economics. The further back a recycling loop goes up the flowchart, the more expensive the recycling process generally becomes. And because each stage of the flowchart adds value to the materials passing through, materials being recycled back to the front end have to compete with cheaper materials coming forward.

A critical factor in LCA is the definition of the system boundary within which all consumptions and emissions are evaluated, and outside which any consumptions and emissions are considered to be part of the general environment in which the system operates. All too often in the past, the process activity within a factory fence has been optimized with little or no regard to what happens upstream and downstream in the environmental life cycle of a final product. In the LCA of dyed fabrics, for example, the factories upstream of the dyehouse which produce acetate, polyester and nylon fabrics, dyes and other chemicals must also be included within the material and product manufacturing categories. The 'cradles' might include oil and gas reservoirs and the 'graves' would almost certainly include landfill sites where the finished goods are disposed of.

Case study examples of the use of LCA for pollution prevention are provided by Allen et al[31].

6. EXAMPLE WORKSHEETS

In the two documents produced by its Hazardous Waste Engineering Research Laboratory (Office of Research and Development)[2,3], the US Environmental Protection Agency makes extensive use of worksheets for the assessment and evaluation phases of its waste minimization methodology. Table 6 lists these worksheets according to the particular phase in the methodology. Worksheets 9, 10 and 14 are reproduced on pages 59–69.

TABLE 6
List of waste minimization assessment worksheets
(source: US Environmental Protection Agency Manual[2] and Guide[3])

Number and title	Purpose/remarks
1. Assessment overview	Summarizes the overall assessment procedure.
2. Programme organization	Records key members in the waste minimization programme task force and the waste minimization assessment and evaluation teams. Also records the relevant organization.
3. Assessment and evaluation team make-up	Lists names of assessment and evaluation team members as well as duties. Includes a list of potential departments to consider when selecting the teams.
4. Site description	Lists background information about the facility, including location, products and operations.
5. Personnel	Records information about the personnel who work in the area to be assessed.
6. Process information	This is a check list of useful process information to look for before starting the assessment.
7. Input materials summary	Records input material information for a specific production or process area. This includes name, supplier, hazardous component or properties, cost, delivery and shelf-life information, and possible substitutes.

Continued overleaf

TABLE 6 (continued)

Number and title	Purpose/remarks
8. Products summary	Identifies hazardous components, production rate, revenues and other information about products.
9. Individual waste streams characterization	Records source, hazard, generation rate, disposal cost and method of treatment or disposal for each waste stream.
10. Waste stream summary	Summarizes all of the information collected for each waste stream. This sheet is also used to prioritize waste streams to assess.
11. Option generation	Records options proposed during brainstorming or nominal group technique sessions. Includes the rationale for proposing each option.
12. Option description	Describes and summarizes information about a proposed option. Also notes approval of promising options.
13. Options evaluation by weighted sum method	Used for screening options using the weighted sum method.
14. Technical feasibility	Detailed check list for performing a technical evaluation of a waste minimization option. This worksheet is divided into sections for equipment-related options, personnel/procedural-related options and materials-related options.
15. Cost information	Detailed list of capital and operating cost information for use in the economic evaluation of an option.
16. Profitability Worksheet No 1: pay-back period	Based on the capital and operating cost information developed from Worksheet 15, this worksheet is used to calculate the pay-back period.
17. Profitability Worksheet No 2: cash flow for NPV and IRR	This worksheet is used to develop cash flows for calculating net present value (NPV) or internal rate of return (IRR).
18. Project summary	Summarizes important tasks to be performed during the implementation of an option. This includes deliverable, responsible person, budget and schedule.
19. Option performance	Records material balance information for evaluating the performance of an implemented option.

Firm _____	**Waste Minimization Assessment**	Prepared by _____
Site _____		Checked by _____
Date _____	Project No _____	Sheet <u>1</u> of <u>4</u> Page__of__

| WORKSHEET **9a** | INDIVIDUAL WASTE STREAM CHARACTERIZATION | ♺**EPA** |

1. **Waste stream name/ID:** _____**Stream number** _____

    Process unit/operation _____

2. **Waste characteristics** (attached additional sheets with composition data, as necessary)

    ☐ gas   ☐ liquid   ☐ solid   ☐ mixed phase

    Density, lb/cuft _____High heating value, Btu/lb _____

    Viscosity/consistency

    pH _____Flash point _____% water _____

3. **Waste leaves process as:**

    ☐ air emission   ☐ waste water   ☐ solid waste   ☐ hazardous waste

4. **Occurrence**

    ☐ continuous

    ☐ discrete

    discharge triggered by   ☐ chemical analysis

    ☐ other (describe)

    Type: ☐ periodic _____length of period: _____

    ☐ sporadic (irregular occurrence)

    ☐ non-recurrent

5. **Generation rate**

    Annual_____lbs per year

    Maximum _____lbs per _____

    Average_____lbs per _____

    Frequency _____batches per _____

    Batch size _____average _____range

59

Firm _____	**Waste Minimization Assessment**	Prepared by _____
Site _____	Proc. Unit/Oper. _____	Checked by _____
Date _____	Project No _____	Sheet 2 of 4 Page__of__

| WORKSHEET **9b** | INDIVIDUAL WASTE STREAM CHARACTERIZATION | ❧EPA |

(continued)

6.   Waste origins/sources

Fill out this worksheet to identify the origin of the waste. If the waste is a mixture of waste streams, fill out a sheet for each of the individual waste streams.

Is the waste mixed with other wastes?   ☐ Yes   ☐ No

Describe how the waste is generated.

_____
_____
_____
_____
_____
_____
_____
_____
_____
_____
_____
_____
_____
_____
_____
_____
_____
_____
_____
_____
_____
_____
_____
_____

Example: Formation and removal of an undesirable compound, removal of an unconverted input material, depletion of a key component (eg drag-out), equipment cleaning waste, obsolete input material, spoiled batch and production run, spill or leak cleanup, evaporative loss, breathing or venting losses, etc

Firm _____ Site _____ Date _____	**Waste Minimization Assessment** Proc. Unit/Oper. _____ Project No _____	Prepared by _____ Checked by _____ Sheet 3 of 4 Page__of__

WORKSHEET **9c**	INDIVIDUAL WASTE STREAM CHARACTERIZATION	❧EPA

(continued)

Waste stream _____

7.   **Management method**

Leaves site in   ☐ bulk _____
☐ roll off bins _____
☐ 55 gal drums _____
☐ other (describe) _____

Disposal frequency _____
_____

Applicable regulations [1] _____
_____

Regulatory classification [2] _____
_____

Managed   ☐ onsite   ☐ offsite
☐ commercial TSDF   _____
☐ own TSDF   _____
☐ other (describe)   _____
_____

Recycling   ☐ direct use/re-use   _____
☐ energy recovery   _____
☐ redistilled   _____
☐ other (describe)   _____

reclaimed material returned to site?
☐ Yes   ☐ No   ☐ used by others
residue yield _____
residue disposal/repository _____
_____

Note[1]   list federal, state and local regulations (eg RCRA, TSCA, etc)
Note[2]   list pertinent regulatory classification (eg RCRA — listed K011 waste, etc)

Firm _____	**Waste Minimization Assessment**	Prepared by _____
Site _____	Proc. Unit/Oper. _____	Checked by _____
Date _____	Project No _____	Sheet 4 of 4 Page__of__

| WORKSHEET **9d** | INDIVIDUAL WASTE STREAM CHARACTERIZATION | ♻ **EPA** |

(continued)

Waste stream _____

7.   Management method (continued)

Treatment

☐ biological _____
☐ oxidation/reduction _____
☐ incineration _____
☐ pH adjustment _____
☐ precipitation _____
☐ solidification _____
☐ other (describe) _____
  _____

☐ residue disposal/repository _____
  _____

Final disposition

☐ landfill _____
☐ pond _____
☐ lagoon _____
☐ deep well _____
☐ ocean _____
☐ other (describe) _____
  _____

Costs as of _____(quarter and year)

Cost element	Unit price $ per___	Reference/source
Onsite storage & handling		
Pretreatment		
Container		
Transportation fee		
Disposal fee		
Local taxes		
State tax		
Federal tax		
Total disposal cost		

Firm _____	**Waste Minimization Assessment**	Prepared by _____
Site _____	Proc. Unit/Oper. _____	Checked by _____
Date _____	Project No _____	Sheet 1 of 1 Page__of__

WORKSHEET **10**	WASTE STREAM SUMMARY	EPA

Attribute	Description [1]		
	Stream no.____	Stream no.____	Stream no.____
Waste ID/name:			
Source/origin			
Component/or property of concern			
Annual generation rate (units____)			
Overall			
Component(s) of concern			
Cost of disposal			
Unit cost ($ per_____)			
Overall (per year)			
Method of Management [2]			

Priority rating criteria [3]	Relative Wt (W)	Rating (R)	R x W	Rating (R)	R x W	Rating (R)	R x W
Regulatory compliance							
Treatment/disposal cost							
Potential liability							
Waste quantity generated							
Waste hazard							
Safety hazard							
Minimization potential							
Potential to remove bottleneck							
Potential by-product recovery							
Sum of priority rating scores		$\sum (R \times W)$		$\sum (R \times W)$		$\sum (R \times W)$	
Priority rank							

Notes: 1. Stream numbers, if applicable, should correspond to those used on process flow diagrams.

     2. For example, sanitary landfill, hazardous waste landfill, onsite recycle, incineration, combustion with heat recovery, distillation, dewatering, etc.

     3. Rate each stream in each category on a scale from 0 (none) to 10 (high).

Firm _____	**Waste Minimization Assessment**	Prepared by _____
Site _____	Proc. Unit/Oper. _____	Checked by _____
Date _____	Project No _____	Sheet <u>1</u> of <u>6</u> Page__of__

| WORKSHEET **14a** | **TECHNICAL FEASIBILITY** | **♻EPA** |

WM Option Description _____

1. **Nature of WM option**
   - ☐ equipment-related
   - ☐ personnel/procedure-related
   - ☐ materials-related

2. **If the option appears technically feasible, state your rationale for this**_____
   _____
   _____

   Is further analysis required?   ☐ Yes   ☐ No
   If yes, continue with this worksheet. If not, skip to worksheet 15.

3. **Equipment-related option**

	Yes	No
Equipment available commercially?	☐	☐ _____
Demonstrated commercially?	☐	☐ _____
In similar application?	☐	☐ _____
Successfully?	☐	☐ _____

   Describe closest industrial analog_____
   _____
   _____

   Describe status of development _____
   _____
   _____

Prospective vendor	Working installation(s)	Contact person(s)	Date contacted [1]

1. Also attach filled out phone conversation notes, installation visit report, etc.

64

Firm _____	**Waste Minimization Assessment**	Prepared by _____
Site _____	Proc. Unit/Oper. _____	Checked by _____
Date _____	Project No _____	Sheet 2 of 6 Page__of__

| WORKSHEET **14b** | **TECHNICAL FEASIBILITY** (continued) | **♻EPA** |

WM Option Description _____

3. **Equipment-related option (continued)**

Performance information required (describe parameters): _____
_____
_____
_____
_____

Scale-up information required (describe): _____
_____
_____
_____
_____

Testing required: ☐ Yes   ☐ No
Scale: ☐ bench   ☐ pilot _____
Test unit available?   ☐ Yes   ☐ No _____
Test parameters (list) _____
_____
_____

Number of test runs: _____
Amount of material(s) required: _____
Testing to be conducted: ☐ in-plant
                                ☐ _____

Facility/product constraints:
   Space requirements _____
   Possible locations within facility _____
_____
_____

65

Firm _____	**Waste Minimization Assessment**	Prepared by _____
Site _____	Proc. Unit/Oper. _____	Checked by _____
Date _____	Project No _____	Sheet 3 of 6 Page__of__

| WORKSHEET **14c** | **TECHNICAL FEASIBILITY** | ♻EPA |

(continued)

WM Option Description _____

2.   **Equipment-related option (continued)**

   Utility requirements:

   Electric power   Volts (AC or DC) _____kW_____

   Process water   Flow _____Pressure _____

   Quality (tap, demin, etc) _____

   Cooling water   Flow _____Pressure _____

   Temp in _____Temp out_____

   Coolant/heat transfer fluid _____

   Temp in _____Temp out_____

   Duty _____

   Steam   Pressure _____Temp_____

   Duty _____Flow _____

   Fuel   Type _____Flow _____

   Duty _____

   Plant air _____Flow _____

   Inert gas _____Flow _____

Estimated delivery time (after award of contract) _____

Estimated installation time _____

Installation dates _____

Estimated production downtime_____

Will production be otherwise affected? Explain the effect and impact on production. _____
_____
_____
_____

Will product quality be affected? Explain the effect on quality. _____
_____
_____
_____

Firm _____	**Waste Minimization Assessment**	Prepared by _____
Site _____	Proc. Unit/Oper. _____	Checked by _____
Date _____	Project No _____	Sheet <u>4</u> of <u>6</u> Page__of__

| WORKSHEET **14d** | **TECHNICAL FEASIBILITY** | **❧EPA** |

(continued)

WM Option Description _____

3. **Equipment-related option (continued)**

    Will modifications to work flow or production procedures be required? Explain_____
    _____
    _____
    _____
    _____

    Operator and maintenance training requirements
    Number of people to be trained _____   ☐ Onsite _____
    _____   ☐ Offsite _____
    Duration of training _____

    Describe catalyst, chemicals, replacement parts, or other supplies required.

Item	Rate or frequency of replacement	Supplier, address

    Does the option meet government and company safety and health requirements?
    ☐ Yes   ☐ No   Explain_____
    _____
    _____

    How is service handled (maintenance and technical assistance)? Explain _____
    _____
    _____
    _____

    What warranties are offered? _____
    _____
    _____

Firm _____	**Waste Minimization Assessment**	Prepared by _____
Site _____	Proc. Unit/Oper. _____	Checked by _____
Date _____	Project No _____	Sheet <u>5</u> of <u>6</u> Page__of__

WORKSHEET
14e

TECHNICAL FEASIBILITY

😊EPA

(continued)

WM Option Description _____

3. **Equipment-related option (continued)**

   Describe any additional storage or material handling requirements._____

   _____
   _____
   _____

   Describe any additional laboratory or analytical requirements._____

   _____
   _____
   _____

4. **Personnel/procedure-related changes**

   Affected departments/areas _____

   _____
   _____

   Training requirements_____

   _____
   _____

   Operating instruction changes. Describe responsible departments. _____

   _____
   _____

5. **Materials-related changes (Note: if substantial changes in equipment are required, then handle the option as an equipment-related one)**

	Yes	No
Has the new material been demonstrated commercially?	☐	☐
In a similar application?	☐	☐
Successfully?	☐	☐

   Describe closest application. _____

   _____
   _____

68

Firm _____	**Waste Minimization Assessment**	Prepared by _____
Site _____	Proc. Unit/Oper. _____	Checked by _____
Date _____	Project No _____	Sheet <u>6</u> of <u>6</u> Page__of__

| WORKSHEET **14f** | **TECHNICAL FEASIBILITY** | EPA |

(continued)

WM Option Description _____

4.   **Materials-related changes (continued)**

   Affected departments/areas _____

   _____

   _____

   _____

   Will production be affected? Explain the effect and impact on production. _____

   _____

   _____

   _____

   Will product quality be affected? Explain the effect and the impact on product quality. _____

   _____

   _____

   _____

   Will additional storage, handling or other ancilliary equipment be required? Explain. _____

   _____

   _____

   _____

   Describe any training or procedure changes that are required. _____

   _____

   _____

   _____

   Describe any material testing program that will be required. _____

   _____

   _____

   _____

69

7.   TYPICAL CAUSES AND SOURCES OF WASTE

Tables 7 and 8 are designed to help the development of a waste minimization programme. Table 7 lists typical wastes from plant operations. Table 8 lists typical causes and controlling factors in waste generation.

TABLE 7
Typcial wastes from plant operations
(source: US Environmental Protection Agency Manual[2] and Guide[3]

Plant function	Location/operation	Potential waste material
Material receiving	Loading docks, incoming pipelines, receiving areas	Packaging materials, off-spec materials, damaged containers, inadvertent spills, transfer hose emptying
Raw materials and product storage	Tanks, warehouses, drum storage yards, bins, storerooms	Tank bottoms; off-spec and excess materials; spill residues; leaking pumps valves, tanks and pipes; damaged containers; empty containers
Production	Melting, curing, baking, distilling, washing, coating, formulating, reaction, materials handling	Washwater; rinse water; solvents; still bottoms; off-spec products; catalysts; empty containers; sweepings; ductwork clean-out; additives, oil; filters; spill residue; excess materials; process solution dumps; leaking pipes, valves, hoses, tanks and process equipment
Support services	Laboratories	Reagents, off-spec chemicals, samples, empty sample and chemical containers
	Maintenance shops	Solvents, cleaning agents, degreasing sludges, sand-blasting waste, caustic, scrap metal, oils, greases

Continued opposite

TABLE 7 (continued)

Plant function	Location/operation	Potential waste material
Support services (continued)	Garages	Oils, filters, solvents, acids, caustics, cleaning bath sludges, batteries
	Powerhouses/boilers	Fly ash, slag, tube clean-out material, chemical additives, oil, empty containers, boiler blowdown, chemical wastes from water treatment
	Cooling towers	Chemical additives, empty containers, cooling tower blowdown, fan tube oils

TABLE 8
Causes and controlling factors in waste generation
(source: US Environmental Protection Agency Manual[2] and Guide[3]

Waste/ origin	Typical causes	Operational factors	Design factors
Chemical reaction	• Incomplete conversion • By-product formation • Catalyst deactivation (by poisoning or sintering)	• Inadequate temperature control • Inadequate mixing • Poor feed flow control • Poor feed purity control	• Proper reactor design • Proper catalyst selection • Choice of process • Choice of reaction conditions
Contact between aqueous and organic phases	• Condensate from steam jet ejectors • Presence of water as a reaction by-product • Use of water for product rinse • Equipment cleaning • Spill clean-up	• Indiscriminate use of water for cleaning or washing	• Vacuum pumps instead of steam jet ejectors • Choice of process • Use of reboilers instead of steam stripping

Continued overleaf

TABLE 8 (continued)

Waste/ origin	Typical causes	Operational factors	Design factors
Process equipment cleaning	• Presence of residual material • Deposit formation • Use of filter aids • Use of chemical cleaners	• Excessive use of hazardous cleaners • Drainage prior to cleaning • Production scheduling to reduce cleaning frequency • Switch from batch to continuous operation	• Provide wiper blades for reactor and tank inner surface • Use equipment dedication to reduce cross-contamination • Design equipment and piping to minimize hold-up
Heat exchanger cleaning	• Presence of residual material (process side) or scale (cooling water side) • Deposit formation • Use of chemical cleaners	• Inadequate cooling water treatment • Excessive cooling water temperature	• Design for lower film temperature and high turbulence • Controls to prevent cooling water from overheating
Metal parts cleaning	• Disposal of spent solvents, spent cleaning solution, or cleaning sludge	• Indiscriminate use of solvent or water	• Choice between cold dip tank or vapour degreasing • Choice between solvent aqueous cleaning solution
Metal surface treating	• Dragout • Disposal of spent treating solution	• Poor rack maintenance • Excessive rinsing with water • Fast removal of workpiece	• Countercurrent rinsing • Fog rinsing • Dragout collection tanks or trays

Continued opposite

TABLE 8 (continued)

Waste/ origin	Typical causes	Operational factors	Design factors
Disposal of unusable raw materials or off-spec products	• Obsolete raw materials • Off-spec products caused by contamination, improper reactant controls, inadequate pre-cleaning of equipment or workpiece, temperature or pressure excursions	• Poor operator training or supervision • Inadequate quality control • Inadequate production planning and inventory control of feedstocks	• Use of automation • Maximize dedication of equipment to a single function
Clean-up of spills and leaks	• Manual material transfer and handling • Leaking pump seals • Leaking flange gaskets	• Inadequate maintenance • Poor operator training • Lack of attention by operator • Excessive use of water in cleaning	• Choice of gasketing materials • Choice of seals • Use of welded or seal-welded construction
Paint application	• Overspray • Colour change • Clean-up	• Use of solvent-based rather than water-based paint • Spray angle, rate and overlap • Paint solids content	• Automization method (air, pressure or centrifugal) • Electrostatic application • Automate painting to improve application
Paint removal	• Replacing worn coating • Removing defective coating	• Inadequate quality control • Use of solvent strippers	• Use abrasive or cryogenic stripping • Use less hazardous

8. SOURCES OF PRACTICAL WASTE MINIMIZATION TECHNIQUES

Examples of practical techniques are provided in References 1–5, 14–19 and 33.

As a specific example, Table 9 gives a list, taken from the US EPA Draft Guide[3], of waste minimization options which are particularly appropriate to solvent cleaning operations.

TABLE 9

Waste minimization options for solvent cleaning operations (source: US Environmental Protection Agency Guide[3])

Waste	Source/origin	Waste reduction measures	Remarks
Spent solvent	Contaminated solvent from parts cleaning operations	• Use water-soluble cutting fluids instead of oil-based fluids	This could eliminate the need for solvent cleaning
		• Use peel coatings in place of protective oils	
		• Use aqueous cleaners	
		• Use bead blasting for paint stripping	
		• Use cryogenic stripping	
		• Use aqueous paint stripping solutions	
		• Use multi-stage countercurrent cleaning	
		• Prevent cross-contamination	
		• Prevent drag-in from other processes	
		• Ensure prompt removal of sludge from the tank	
		• Reduce the number of different solvents	A single, larger waste that is more amenable to recycling

Continued opposite

TABLE 9 (continued)

Waste	Source/origin	Waste reduction measures	Remarks
Spent solvent (cont'd)	Contaminated solvent from parts cleaning operations	• Install solvent recovery system (ie, distillation unit) • Use old solvent for pre-soak • Change to mechanical cleaning process • Minimize open surface area • Reduce temperature in solvent tank	 Extends life of fresh solvent Less evaporation Less evaporation
Air emissions	Solvent loss from degreasers and cold tanks	• Use roll-type covers, not hinged covers • Increase freeboard height • Install freeboard chillers • Use silhouette entry covers • Avoid rapid insertion and removal of items • Avoid inserting oversized objects into the tank • Allow for proper drainage before removing item • Avoid water contamination of solvent in degreasers • Rinse carbon adsorption unit to reclaim solvent	24–50% reduction in emissions 39% reduction in solvent emissions The speed that items are put into the tank should be less than $0.06\ \mathrm{ms}^{-1}$ Cross-sectional area of the item should be less than 50% of tank area to reduce piston effect
Rinse water	Water rinse to remove solvent carried out with the parts leaving the cleaning tank	• Reduce solvent dragout by proper design and operation of rack system • Install air jets to blow parts dry • Use fog nozzles on rinse tanks • Properly design and operate barrel plating system	The dragout can be substantially reduced for poorly drained parts

Continued overleaf

75

TABLE 9 (continued)

Waste	Source/origin	Waste reduction measures	Remarks
Rinse water (cont'd)	Water rinse to remove solvent carried out with the parts leaving the cleaning tank	• Use countercurrent rinse tanks • Use water sprays on rinse tanks • Recycle and reuse rinse water • Reclaim metals from rinse water • Use deionized water makeup	More efficient rinsing is achieved Reduced contaminant build-up

9.   REFERENCES

1.   IChemE, 1994, Waste Minimization Training Package (IChemE, Rugby, UK).
2.   US Environmental Protection Agency, 1988, *Waste Minimization Opportunity Assessment Manual* (US EPA Hazardous Waste Engineering Research Laboratory, Office of Research and Development, Cincinnati, Ohio, USA).
3.   US Environmental Protection Agency, 1991, *Draft Guide for an Effective Pollution Prevention Program* (US EPA Hazardous Waste Engineering Research Laboratory, Office of Research and Development, Cincinnati, Ohio, USA).
4.   Department of Trade and Industry, 1989, *Cutting your Losses: A Business Guide to Waste Minimization* (Department of Trade and Industry, London, UK).
5.   Department of Trade and Industry, 1992, *Cutting your Losses 2: A Further Guide to Waste Minimization for Business* (Department of Trade and Industry, London, UK).
6.   *Croner's Waste Management*, 1991 plus updates (Croner Publications Ltd, Kingston upon Thames, UK).
7.   Crittenden, B. (Ed), *Management of Waste in the Process Industries* (IChemE, Rugby, UK). Due for publication in mid-1995.
8.   British Standards Institution, 1992, *BS 7750:1992 Specification for Environmental Management Systems*.
9.   Ottewell, S., The club approach to clean-up, *The Chemical Engineer*, 14 October 1993, No. 551, s5.
10. Woolf, G., Waste gets a catalytic response, *The Chemical Engineer*, 28 April 1994, No. 564, 17–18.
11. Clouston, S., 1994, Project Catalyst — a waste minimization demonstration project, in *Water Use and Reuse*, D. Newton and G. Solt (Eds) (IChemE, Rugby, UK).
12. IChemE, 1988, *A Guide to Capital Cost Estimating* (IChemE, Rugby, UK).
13. Allen, D., 1990, *Economic Evaluation of Projects* (IChemE, Rugby, UK).
14. Smith, R. and Petela, E., 1991, Waste minimization in the process industries. Part 1: The problem, *The Chemical Engineer*, 31 October 1991, 24–25.
15. Smith, R. and Petela, E., 1991, Waste minimization in the process industries. Part 2: Reactors, *The Chemical Engineer*, 12 December 1991, 17–23.
16. Smith, R. and Petela, E., 1992, Waste minimization in the process industries. Part 3: Separation and recycle systems, *The Chemical Engineer*, 13 February 1992, 24–28.
17. Smith, R. and Petela, E., 1992, Waste minimization in the process industries. Part 4: Process operations, *The Chemical Engineer*, 9 April 1992, 21–23.
18. Smith, R. and Petela, E., 1992, Waste minimization in the process industries. Part 5: Utility waste, *The Chemical Engineer*, 16 July 1992, 32–35.

19. United Nations Environment Programme, 1993, *Cleaner Production Worldwide* (UNEP Industry and Environment Programme Activity Centre, Paris, France).

20. Hopper, J.R., Yaws, C.L., Ho, T.C. and Vichailak, M., 1993, Waste minimization by process modification, *Waste Management*, 13: 3–14.

21. Douglas, J.M., 1985, A hierarchical procedure for process synthesis, *AIChE J*, 31 (3): 353–362.

22. Douglas, J.M., 1988, *Conceptual Design of Chemical Processes* (McGraw-Hill, New York, USA).

23. Douglas, J.M., 1992, Process synthesis for waste minimization, *Ind Eng Chem Res*, 31 (1): 238–243.

24. Flower, J.R., Bikos, S.C. and Johns, S.W., 1992, A new graphical method for choosing better mass flow sheets for environmentally aware processes, *Effluent Treatment and Waste Minimization, IChemE Symp Series No. 132*, 109–121 (IChemE, Rugby, UK).

25. Bagajewicz, M.J. and Manousiouthakis, V., 1992, Mass/heat exchange representation of distillation networks, *AIChE J*, 38 (11): 1769–1800.

26. El-Halwagi, M.M. and Manousiouthakis, V., 1989, Synthesis of mass exchange networks, *AIChE J*, 35 (8): 1233–1244.

27. El-Halwagi, M.M. and Manousiouthakis, V., 1990, Automatic synthesis of mass exchange networks with single component targets, *Chem Eng Sci*, 45: 2813–2831.

28. El-Halwagi, M.M. and Srinivas, B.K., 1992, Synthesis of reactive mass exchange networks, *Chem Eng Sci*, 47: 2113–2119.

29. Potter, N. and Isalski, H., 1993, Environmental optimization — the Envop technique, *Environmental Protection Bulletin*, No. 026, 17–25.

30. Henstock, M.E., 1993, An analysis of the recycling of LDPE at Alida Recycling Ltd, *Environmental Protection Bulletin*, No. 027, 3–10.

31. Allen, D., Bakshani, N. and Rosselot, K.S., 1992, *Pollution Prevention, Homework and Design Problems for Engineering Curricula* (AIChE, New York, USA).

32. Wentz, C.A., 1989, *Hazardous Waste Management* (McGraw-Hill, New York, USA).

33. Freeman, H.M., 1990, *Hazardous Waste Minimization* (McGraw-Hill, New York, USA).

10. FURTHER READING

Baker, A., Pugh, S. and Durrant, A., 1991, *Final Report on Cleaner Technologies: Stage II Study for the Department of Trade and Industry Environment Unit* (PA Consulting Group, Royston, Hertfordshire, UK).

Barlow, G.N., 1992, An approach to waste minimization, *Environmental Protection Bulletin*, No. 017, 3–12.

Caughlin, R.T., 1993, A study of waste and pollution management in the fine chemicals sector, *MSc Dissertation* (Simon Environmental Technology Centre, UMIST, UK).

Chemical Industries Association, *The Chemical Industry and the Environment — An Agenda for Progress*.

Chemical Industries Association, 1991, *Guidance on Safety, Occupational Health and Envrionmental Protection Auditing*.

Chemical Industries Association, 1992, *Responsible Care Management Systems*.

Chemical Industries Association, 1992, *Guidelines on Waste Management — The Responsible Use of Landfill* (2nd edition).

Cheremisinoff, P. and Ferranti, L., 1992, *Waste Reduction and Pollution Prevention* (Butterworth Heinemann, UK).

Clean Technology Unit, 1993, *Stopping Waste within the Production Process* (based on a report by B.D. Crittenden and S.T. Kolaczkowski) (Science and Engineering Research Council, Swindon, UK).

Cohen, Y. and Allen, D., 1992, An integrated approach to process waste minimization research, *J Hazardous Materials*, 29: 237–253.

CEFIC, 1990, *CEFIC Guidelines on Waste Minimization* (CEFIC, Brussels, Belgium).

Daae, E. and Clift, R., 1994, A life cycle assessment of the implications of paper use and recycling, *Environmental Protection Bulletin*, No. 028, 23–25.

Department of the Environment, 1992, *The UK Environment* (edited by A. Brown *et al*) (HMSO, London, UK).

Department of the Environment, 1992, *Reducing Emissions of Volatile Organic Compounds (VOCs) and Levels of Ground Level Ozone: A UK Strategy*, Consultation Document.

79

Department of the Environment, 1992b, *Waste Management Paper No. 1: Review of Options*, 2nd edition (HMSO, London, UK).

Dyer, A., 1992, Waste not, want not, but why not?, *Process Engineering Environmental Protection*.

Freeman, H.M., 1988, *Standard Handbook of Hazardous Waste Treatment and Disposal* (McGraw-Hill, New York, USA).

Her Majesty's Inspectorate of Pollution, 1994, *Environmental, Economic and BPEO Principles for Integrated Pollution Control*, Discussion document (Her Majesty's Inspectorate of Pollution, London, UK).

Hudson, J.M. and Kornreich, M.R., 1984, *Scoring Systems for Hazard Assessment, in Hazard Assessment of Chemicals. Current Developments*, Volume 3, J. Saxena (Ed) (Academic Press).

Hunter, J.S. and Benforado, D.M., 1987, Life cycle approach to effective waste minimization, *J Air Pollution Control and Hazardous Waste Management*, 37: 1206–1210.

ICC Publishing SA, 1991, *ICC Guide to Effective Environmental Auditing* (ICC, Paris, France).

Johns, W., 1992, Designing an intrinsically 'clean' process, *Process Industry Journal*, November, 19–22.

Kosson, D.S., 1988, Opportunities for research in waste minimization, *Environmental Progress*, 7: 212–214.

LaGrega, M.D., Buckingham, P.L. and Evans, J.C., 1994, *Hazardous Waste Management* (McGraw-Hill, New York, USA).

Masor, K.D., 1993, *The UK Environmental Foresight Project, Volume 1: Preparing for the Future* (HMSO, London, UK).

McBain, D.C., 1990, Chemical assessment, information exchange and the internation register of potentially toxic chemicals (IRPTC), in *The Management of Hazardous Substances in the Environment*, K.I. Zirm and J. Mayer (Eds) (Elsevier Applied Science).

Overcash, M.R., 1986, *Techniques for Industrial Pollution Prevention* (Lewis Publishers, Chelsea, Michigan, USA).

Richmond, J. (Ed), 1990, *Industrial Waste Audit and Reduction Manual: A Practical Guide to Conducting an In-Plant Survey for Waste Reduction* (Ontario Waste Management Corporation, Ontario, Canada).

Shanks and McEwan Group plc, 1993, *Best Practicable Environmental Option for the Disposal of Hazardous Wastes*, Discussion document (Shanks and McEwan, Aylesbury, UK).

Wang, Y.P. and Smith, R., 1994, Wastewater minimization, Chem Eng Sci, 49 (7): 981–1006.

APPENDIX — LIST OF ACRONYMS

BATNEEC — best available techniques not entailing excessive cost
BPEO — best practicable environmental option
BS — British Standard

CIMAH — Control of Industrial Major Accident Hazards
COPA 1974 — Control of Pollution Act 1974
COSHH — Control of Substances Hazardous to Health

DoE — Department of the Environment (UK)
DTI — Department of Trade and Industry (UK)

EC — European Community
Envop — environmental optimization
EPA — Environmental Protection Agency (USA)
EPA 1990 — Environmental Protection Act 1990
EU — European Union

Hazan — hazard analysis
Hazop — hazard and operability study
HEN — heat exchange network
HMIP — Her Majesty's Inspectorate of Pollution

IChemE — Institution of Chemical Engineers
IPC — integrated pollution control
IRR — internal rate of return

LCA — life cycle analysis
LDP — liquid dispersion polymers

MEN — mass exchange network

NPV — net present value